Global Criter

The 12
CORE FUNCTIONS
of the Substance
Abuse Counselor

Fifth Edition

John W. Herdman, Ph.D., LADC

ISBN 0-9768341-2-X

ISBN13: 978-0-9768341-2-0

For Information
John W. Herdman, Ph.D., LADC
Parallels: Pathways to Change
4706 S. 48th Street
Lincoln, NE 68516
402-489-9792 – Office
866-489-9792 – Toll Free
402-489-9793 – Fax
johnh@parallelslincoln.com
www.ParallelsLincoln.com
www.johnherdman.com

Printing: 7 6   Year: 08

To Nancy,

May we keep on dreaming!

Love John

About the Author

John Herdman, Ph.D., LADC is a Nebraska licensed psychologist, a licensed alcohol and drug counselor, and a certified school psychologist. He has over 34 years of school, military, counseling, and consulting experience. Dr. Herdman has conducted training nationally and internationally on a variety of topics. His professional training has had a major emphasis upon solution-focused and cognitive-behavioral approaches to help clients with problems of everyday living.

In the substance abuse field, Dr. Herdman founded two licensed outpatient treatment facilities in Pennsylvania prior to relocating in Nebraska in 1993. Dr. Herdman has been a technical assistance consultant to the Office of Substance Abuse Prevention (OSAP), now the Center for Substance Abuse Prevention (CSAP) in the area of evaluation design for substance abuse prevention projects and has extensive experience with needs assessments for school-aged children and for business and industry. As an Air Force Reserve Officer, Lt. Col. Herdman retired in January of 2000 as an Individual Mobilization Augmentee to the Chief, Human Resources Development Division at Headquarters Air Force, the Pentagon. He had been instrumental in helping the Air Force with their drug and alcohol counselor certification and admission to the International Certification and Reciprocity Consortium (IC&RC/AODA). He served as secretary of the IC&RC for two terms and was a co-chair of the Case Presentation Method (CPM) committee, and was a CPM Training Supervisor. He recently served as a Subject Matter Expert (SME) for the IC&RC/AODA for the Advanced Alcohol and Other Drug Abuse credential revision. His first book, *Global Criteria: The 12 Core Functions of the Substance Abuse Counselor*, was very well accepted as a preparatory guide for helping counselors reach their goal of certification or licensure as a substance abuse counselor. This is the fifth edition of that book and is a major revision of the Fourth Edition.

Dr. Herdman has all three of his degrees from Penn State University. He is currently a licensed psychologist and consultant in private practice in Lincoln, Nebraska. He owns Parallels, a mental health and drug and alcohol treatment program in Lincoln. He continues to offer workshops across the country and internationally on not only the core functions and clinical supervision, but also in cognitive-behavioral counseling skills and brief therapy techniques for substance abuse counselors and other topics. In 2007 he published his second book, *A Rational Workbook for Recovery from Addictions*. Instructors and readers of this book are invited to correspond with Dr. Herdman regarding additions and areas for improvement in this text for future editions. Dr. Herdman is available for group and individual consultation. His workshop on the core functions is a one day training. Contact him for the schedule of trainings or to arrange a workshop in your area. If you would like to be included on Dr. Herdman's mailing list, please e-mail him at jherdman@binary.net.

John W. Herdman, Ph.D., LADC
4706 S. 48th Street
Lincoln, NE 68516
402-489-9792
e-mail: jherdman@binary.net
web site: http://www.The EncouragementPlace.com

Acknowledgments

Some of the information used on the history of CRC/NCRC/IC&RC is used with permission of the Wisconsin Alcohol and Drug Counselor Certification Board; Jeff Pearcy, executive director; and Irene McMackin, communications manager.

If it were not for the response of counselors in the drug and alcohol treatment field to previous editions, this book would have gone away like so many others. I want to thank all workshop attendees, students, and counselors who have used this book to prepare for the certification examination and to provide quality supervision to the next generation of substance abuse counselors. Writing this book has been one long positive reinforcement for me. I feel like I touch a person's life in a positive way when I hear a comment about how the book helped reduce anxiety for the exam or how the material is easy to understand. I want to thank all of you. I would also like to thank the IC&RC certification boards and college training programs and the individual professors that promote this book and see its benefits for counselors as they prepare for the substance abuse counselor profession.

I would like to thank Dave and Erin Hilsabeck for their effort in proofreading this Fifth Edition. Finally, I would like to thank the International Certification and Reciprocity Consortium (IC&RC) for permission to use the tasks within the eight domains identified in the Certified Alcohol and Other Drug Abuse Counselor Job Task Analysis Report 2008.

Contents

Introduction

Global Criteria: The 12 Core Functions of the Substance Abuse Counselor (Fifth Edition) is a major re-write of the previous editions. It continues to focus on improving the initial and ongoing professional development of substance abuse counselors. In the Fifth Edition I have incorporated the information from TAP 21 and the tasks identified in the most recent Certified Alcohol and Other Drug Abuse Counselor Job Task Analysis Report 2008 completed by the International Certification and Reciprocity Consortium (IC&RC). As a licensed alcohol and drug counselor and licensed psychologist, I am an advocate for professional competence. I view the International Certification and Reciprocity Consortium (IC&RC) standards for certification as a necessary, important, and critical element for protection of the public, the individual client, their families, and the communities that the counselor serves. I have been pleased and impressed with the IC&RC efforts to ensure competence of entry-level alcohol and drug abuse counselors. Some states and certification bodies have even higher education and/or standards for conveying entry-level credentials. These can only increase competence levels as well.

It is my hope that *Global Criteria: The 12 Core Functions of the Substance Abuse Counselor (Fifth Edition)* will increase the entry-level competence of counselors seeking certification or licensure as alcohol and drug abuse counselors. This book discusses the core functions and the global criteria of the substance abuse counselor, and relates to both the TAP 21 proficiencies and the Performance Domains from the Certified Alcohol and Other Drug Abuse Counselor Job Task Analysis Report 2008 of IC&RC. The IC&RC has set the standards for entry level counselors and one requirement includes 300 hours supervised by a certified substance abuse counselor with at least 10 hours in each of the 12 core functions. It is incumbent on the supervisor of these counselors in training to educate and develop the professional skills of these counselors in order to insure their competence and their preparation for the written examination that includes both knowledge and skills and their careers as a substance abuse counselor.

The new examination of the IC&RC is now meant to evaluate applicants for certification as alcohol and drug abuse counselors in both knowledge and skills. This book can be used by professors and instructors in counselor training programs and by supervisors in treatment programs to prepare trainees for a professional career as an alcohol and drug abuse counselor. I hope that this book becomes a resource book on every counselor's shelf, a book that is used not only for individual professional growth but also for sharing with other members of the treatment team.

Acronyms

AA – Alcoholics Anonymous

ADA – Americans with Disabilities Act

ADS – Alcohol Dependence Scale

AEQ – Alcohol Expectancy Questionnaire

AMA – Against Medical Advice

AODA – Alcohol and Other Drug Abuse

AAODA – Advanced Alcohol and Other Drug Abuse

ASI – Addiction Severity Index

AUI – Alcohol Use Inventory

CAS – Columbia Assessment Services

CPM – Case Presentation Method

CRC – Certification Reciprocity Consortium

CSAP – Center for Substance Abuse Prevention

CSAT – Center for Substance Abuse Treatment

DSM-IV – *Diagnostic and Statistical Manual,* Fourth edition

DSM-IV TR – *Diagnostic and Statistical Manual,* Fourth edition Text Revision

IC&RC – International Certification Reciprocity Consortium

JTA – Job Task Analysis

MAST – Michigan Alcoholism Screening Test

MCMI-III – Million Clinical Multiaxial Inventory-III

MMPI-2 – Minnesota Multiphasic Personality Inventory-2

NCADI – National Clearinghouse for Alcohol and Drug Information

NCRC – National Certification Reciprocity Consortium

NIAAA – National Institute on Alcoholism and Alcohol Abuse

OSAP – Office of Substance Abuse Prevention

SAAST – Self-Administered Alcoholism Screening Test

SASSI – Substance Abuse Subtle Screening Inventory

SKA – Skills, Knowledges, and Attitudes

SME – Subject Matter Expert

SOAP – Subjective, Objective, Assessment, and Plan

TAP – Technical Assistance Publication

TIPs – Treatment Improvement Protocols

Chapter 1 - Certification History

Since its founding in 1979, the Certification Reciprocity Consortium/Alcohol and Other Drug Abuse, Inc. (CRC/AODA) has experienced significant growth in membership and has undergone two additional name changes. The CRC board of directors approved the first name change to the National Certification Reciprocity Consortium (NCRC) in 1990 to reflect the national focus and growth of the consortium. With the admission of Canada the NCRC became the International Certification Reciprocity Consortium (ICRC) effective January 1, 1993. By May 1993 a second country, Sweden, was admitted to membership with the prospect of more countries and other states of the United States seeking membership. As of this fifth edition, there are more than 73 certification boards in IC&RC. This includes seven countries, 41 U.S. states, three U.S. military services, seven Indian Health Services (HIS) boards, and two other boards. To view the most current listing of IC&RC boards, you can visit www.icrcaoda.org/memberboards.cfm. The IC&RC's mission is to establish, monitor, and advance reciprocal competency standards for AODA professionals and to support the member boards which serve the public.

Irene McMackin, communications manager for the Wisconsin Alcohol and Drug Counselor Certification Board, provided the following newsletter clip on the CRC:

> *Dateline, April 9, 1979 . . . Alcoholism counselor certification authorities from Wisconsin, Indiana, and Michigan have completed a reciprocity agreement for certified alcoholism counselors practicing in the three states. The agreement will become effective July 1, 1979, pending ratification of the three state's certification boards.*

The above is quoted from a release sent to alcohol and drug abuse publications throughout the nation. They mark the birth of the now large and influential IC&RC with 47 members.

The original agreement was signed in the Brothers of the Holy Cross Center in South Bend, Indiana. Back then it was a great place to meet until the membership grew too large. Room and board cost eight dollars a day; food was always available, even at 3 a.m. Groups could work through the night in conference rooms. Those early work sessions were marathons.

The requirements for membership were worded and reworded. The torturous job of putting together the entire case presentation method and the original pool of questions were wrestled to completion accompanied by late night lullabies of a popcorn popper and a percolator.

As the membership grew, more and more states showed interest. Representatives came to meetings and left with membership in mind.

The first NCRC office was located with the Wisconsin Certification Board in Waukesha. By early 1984, Consortium membership had grown to 19 states. Regional groups were formed.

While the Consortium grew, the National Institute on Alcoholism and Alcohol Abuse (NIAAA) continued its struggle to establish a national credential standard. One firm's contract was canceled, a second, then a third firm slogged through attempts to finish the job.

Meanwhile, the Consortium was beginning work on standards headed toward national acceptance. The following is from a certification publication from the early 1980's:

> *Speaking of the defunct A. T. Kearney contract, their failure to complete their contract after spending a year of work and almost $300,000 is mighty interesting.*
>
> *The Consortium has completed a recertification process, developed a written case presentation and oral interview, and published a newsletter. Consortium member states grant unequivocal reciprocity to each other state's counselors who hold the same type of credential. And their budget wouldn't keep a consulting firm in paper clips.*

Although the CRC was founded in 1979, the representatives from Indiana, Michigan, and Wisconsin first began discussions in April 1977. Standards for certification issues and possibilities of interstate reciprocity were discussed. The CRC Committee on Evaluation began work in January 1980 with the mission to develop a method of evaluation that assessed the competencies of alcohol and drug abuse counselors that could be used by all members without compromising the procedures. The committee defined knowledge and skills needed for counselor competence and listed the functions and duties that alcohol and drug abuse counselors perform. This was the field's first effort at a job analysis or role delineation and resulted in the development of the "12 core functions" that have become the foundation upon which counselors are trained and evaluated.

The committee developed a manual that detailed the Case Presentation Method (CPM) that included requirements for a counselor applicant for certification to prepare a written case, and pass an oral interview (examination) by answering one question in each of the 12 core functions from a pool of questions. The manual served as a training tool for CPM evaluators.

The Birch and Davis Study. In 1984 the NIAAA published the *Development of Model Professional Standards for Counselor Credentialling*. This has become known as the Birch and Davis Study[1], named after the principal authors. In the executive summary of the report, the project set out to develop three major products. The first product was a core set of counselor job tasks. The second was a core set of knowledge and skills reflecting the competencies that the counseling field expected of counselors. And the third was guidelines on techniques for assessing the competencies of individuals seeking counselor certification. The Birch and Davis

---

[1] Birch and Davis Corporation (1986). *Development of Model Professional Standards for Counselor Credentialing.* Dubuque, IA: Kendall/Hunt Publishing.

Study was the first detailed job analysis or role delineation for the alcohol and drug abuse counselor field.

Role Delineation Study for AODA Counselors by the NCRC[2]. In May 1990, the Written Test Committee of the NCRC began in earnest to pursue the development of a national examination for alcohol and drug abuse counselors. The message in many of the meetings was that a national test was needed and that it must be legally defensible and professionally sound. For many on the committee, education was needed to explain legal defensibility and also the necessary psychometric properties needed to make a test professionally sound.

One of the first steps needed to legally defend a test is whether the test is based upon an up-to-date job analysis that helps to establish test validity. Psychometrically, test validation is the way in which a test developer ensures that the competency to be inferred from a test is really measured by the test questions asked. A test is valid if the test measures what it is supposed to measure, i.e., it evaluates the knowledge required to be a competent alcohol and drug abuse counselor. As a consortium of certifying boards, the NCRC had to determine what skills, knowledge, and abilities are needed to perform competently in the alcohol and drug abuse counselor field and thus protect the public from the incompetent counselor.

The NCRC contracted with Columbia Assessment Services, Inc. (CAS) to develop, score, and administer the national examination for member certifying bodies of the NCRC. CAS is a full-service testing company providing licensure, certification, and specialty examinations for associations, state boards, governmental agencies, and corporations. CAS's first step was to conduct a role delineation study. As mentioned previously, the CRC had developed the 12 Core Functions for alcohol and drug abuse counselors in 1980. The Birch and Davis study was published in 1984. Neither the 12 Core Functions nor the Birch and Davis study could be legally defended as "up-to-date."

In conducting the role delineation study, CAS gathered together a 13-member panel of "Subject Matter Experts (SMEs) who were all certified as alcohol and drug abuse counselors. The panel was a cross-section of counselors representative of different geographic regions as well as diversity in gender, age, racial and cultural experiences, treatment modalities, and experience levels. This panel of SMEs determined that the following five major task areas were appropriate for the alcohol and drug abuse counselor profession:

      1. Assessment

      2. Counseling

      3. Case Management

---

[2] International Certification and Reciprocity Consortium (ICRC)/Alcohol and Other Drug Abuse (1991). *Role Delineation Study for Alcohol and Other Drug Abuse Counselors*. Raleigh, NC: ICRC.

4. Education

5. Professional Responsibilities

These five task areas have been termed the Five Performance Domains. The panel then delineated tasks for each domain and generated a list of skills and knowledge required for competent performance of the tasks by alcohol and drug abuse counselors. The panel then evaluated each domain and task as to its importance to an entry-level alcohol and drug abuse counselor, its criticality (extent to which inability to perform the task would cause harm to a client), and the frequency with which a "typical" alcohol and drug abuse counselor would perform the task. Test items were then developed to reflect the knowledge expected of a counselor in each of the domains. The reliability of the written examination was enhanced with the evaluation of five performance domains rather than 12 core functions. However, the relationship of the performance domains to the core functions is very important and will be detailed later in the discussion of the Case Presentation Method (CPM) revision project.

In determining the five performance domains and identifying the tasks (knowledge and skills) of the alcohol and drug abuse counselor, this panel had defined the role of an alcohol and drug abuse counselor in their profession. This role delineation conducted in 1990 stood as the job analysis for counselors until 1996 when the IC&RC conducted another role delineation study. A current role delineation study or job analysis is necessary for continued validation of the written (and oral) examinations and is required for maintaining the IC&RC's place in establishing standards for the alcohol and drug abuse counselor profession.

In order to meet its mission to establish, monitor, and advance reciprocal competency standards for AODA professionals, the IC&RC had to look at its certification procedures, especially in the area of evaluation of competence. The newly developed written examination is meant to evaluate alcohol and drug abuse counselor, aptly done with a multiple-choice testing format. A related but independent area of competence, long recognized as counselor skills rather than mere knowledge, was the oral examination or Case Presentation Method (CPM). The CPM has been recognized as the method to evaluate the alcohol and drug abuse counselor's skills in the 12 core functions of the counselor.

The Relationship between the 12 Core Functions and the Five Performance Domains:

Domains

Assessment	Counseling	Case Mgmt	Education	Professional Responsibility
Screening	Counseling	Case Mgmt	Client Education	Counseling
Intake	Orientation	Referral		Intake
Assessment	Crisis Intervention	Reports & Record Keeping		Consultation
Referral	Referral	Consultation		Referral

Consultation	Treatment Planning	Orientation		Orientation
Treatment Planning	Client Education	Client Education		Screening
Reports & Record Keeping	Consultation	Assessment		Reports & Record Keeping

The CPM Revision Project. Following the implementation of the NCRC's national written examination, the NCRC board of directors again contracted with CAS to review and revise the current oral examination, known as the CPM, used by all certifying bodies of the NCRC. As a member of the NCRC/CPM Committee, this author was involved in the revision project from the initial review meeting held in Washington, D.C., in April 1992, to the completion of the project in March 1993.

The purpose of the revision project was to document the validity of the CPM in light of the NCRC's Role Delineation Study, enhance standardization, and provide a structure for enhancing and estimating the CPM's reliability. There were several major phases of the revision project as follows:

   1. Validation of the CPM

   2. Developing and Validating Basic Criteria for Evaluation and Scoring

   3. Revising and Validating the Pool of Questions

   4. Planning an Effective Evaluator Training Program

As a result of the revision project a *Skills Catalog* was developed to serve as the logical and analytical basis for the CPM's validity. Additionally, the expert panel developed and weighted set of global criteria that provides the structure for scoring the oral examination. Information and discussion of these global criteria are thoroughly discussed in the following chapters.

The CPM revision panel significantly streamlined the pool of questions that applicant counselors must respond to in order to allow the applicant to display competence in the core function and global criteria regardless of the question asked in the core function area. In 1996 the IC&RC streamlined the pool of questions even more. Now there is just one general question for each of the 12 core functions. The applicant is directed to address the core function and each global criterion and to provide complete answers with enough detail no matter how the question is worded. While the written case itself would not be evaluated, the panel recommended that the written case presentation still be required as a way for an applicant to organize his or her thinking about a specific case. Since the written case would not be evaluated, there was no need to establish its validity and reliability.

A key component to a test's reliability is the standardization of scoring. Thus, a *Trainer's Manual* and the IC&RC's *CPM Evaluator Training Video* were developed in order to incorporate all current aspects of the CPM process and to train evaluators to score the CPM reliably. Thus the implementation of the CPM is uniform no matter where in the world it is administered.

Role Delineation Study for AODA Counselors by the IC&RC/AODA (1996)[3].
In order to maintain the validity of the IC&RC written and oral examinations, the IC&RC began another role delineation study or job analysis in October 1995. In the six years since the previous role delineation study, the role of the alcohol and drug abuse counselor has expanded. Although the scope of practice varies across certification boards, the role has broadened to include greater assessment and placement decision making, more counseling responsibility, and greater collaboration with other disciplines. Cultural sensitivity has increased and counselors are expected to be more culturally aware and competent. Education requirements and specific competencies have expanded to coincide with increased counselor responsibilities.

The 1996 study maintained five performance domains. The study changed the fourth domain from "Education" to "Client, Family, and Community Education" to reflect more clearly the counselor's role in the provision of client education.

In 1996, the International Certification and Reciprocity Consortium (IC&RC/AODA) brought together a national leadership group to evaluate the need for model addiction counselor training. After careful thought, the group concluded that much of the work to define such a curriculum standard had already been accomplished by the ATTC National Curriculum Committee and the IC&RC in the National Curriculum Committee's Addiction Counselor Competencies and the IC&RC's 1996 Role Delineation Study, respectively.

Technical Assistance Publication 21 (TAP 21). In 1998, the Substance Abuse and Mental Health Services Administration (SAMHSA) and the Center for Substance Abuse Treatment (CSAT) published Addiction Counseling Competencies: The Knowledges, Skills, and Attitudes of Professional Practice (The Competencies) as Technical Assistance Publication (TAP) 21. Developed by the National Curriculum Committee of the Addiction Technology Transfer Center (ATTC) Network, TAP 21 identifies 123 competencies that are essential to the effective practice of counseling for psychoactive substance use disorders. TAP 21 also presents the knowledges, skills, and attitudes (KSAs) counselors need to become fully proficient in each competency.

The National Curriculum Committee revised TAP 21 in 2000 based on surveys and the feedback of dedicated addiction practice and education professionals; however, this revision was never published.

[3] International Certification and Reciprocity Consortium (ICRC)/Alcohol and Other Drug Abuse (1996). *Role Delineation Study for Alcohol and Other Drug Abuse Counselors*. Raleigh, NC: ICRC.

A new Update Committee was convened in 2005 to update the revised 2000 edition with literature published between 2000 and 2005. The Update Committee consisted of some of the original members from the National Curriculum Committee; representatives from NAADAC—The Association for Addiction Professionals, the Center for Substance Abuse Treatment, the Center for Mental Health Services, the Center for Substance Abuse Prevention, the National Association for Children of Alcoholics, and the Annapolis Coalition; treatment providers; and experts in addiction research. The current updated edition retains all of the feedback-based improvements of the 2000 revised version and added relevant literature published after 2000. In addition, the competencies and KSAs of several practice dimensions, in particular those that address clinical evaluation and treatment planning, were rewritten to reflect current best practices.

TAP 21 identifies eight (8) core domains as follows:

I. Clinical Evaluation
II. Treatment Planning
III. Referral
IV. Service Coordination
V. Counseling
VI. Client, Family, and Community Education
VII. Documentation
VIII. Professional and Ethical Responsibilities

CPM Revision Project (2002-2005). Over time there is a phenomenon in psychometrics called "examiner drift." In the more than 10 years of the revised CPM there have been thousands of applicants evaluated by hundreds of trained evaluators around the world. The original groups of trained evaluators were instructed to "Go out and train others." This has happened. Over time there has been a "drift" in what CPM evaluators have considered acceptable or passing when an applicant for certification provides a response to the global criteria in the CPM. This is a natural consequence of time and human nature. The IC&RC had the responsibility to update the exam across certification boards and thus undertook in 2002 a process to reduce this drift. No wording of the 46 global criteria were proposed to be changed, but the order within a core function changed for a few of the criteria. This was done to provide a more logical flow to an applicant's responses. The committee brought together included some of the original team and some new but experienced faces. We met to discuss each global criterion and to again reach a consensus as to what exactly is required for an entry-level counselor to show competence when answering. I was reminded of Dr. Jim Henderson of Columbia Assessment Services (CAS) telling the original group about peanuts. Dr. Henderson was originally from Georgia and he related the Snickers commercial that said there was a handful of peanuts in every Snickers bar. "Whose hand are we using? – that of a basketball player or that of a child?" It became common for the project group to ask how many peanuts do we need to hear for us to consider a response competent. Over time, various CPM trainers from various certification boards have established the number of peanuts required, but this increases the drift that I mentioned and thus there were slight differences in the CPM across certification board jurisdictions. It was time to get everyone back on the same page. Time, costs, and technology factors led to delays and eventually the IC&RC/AODA Board of Directors decided not to revise the CPM, but rather add to the written examination a skills assessment as a means of evaluation counselor competencies in the 12 core functions, global criteria and the SKAs important to the Substance Abuse counselor field.

About IC&RC, Inc.[4]

The International Certification and Reciprocity Consortium/Alcohol and Other Drug Abuse, Inc. (IC&RC/AODA) is a not-for-profit, voluntary membership organization whose members are alcohol and drug abuse certification boards. Incorporated in 1981, IC&RC currently consists of more than 37,000 alcohol and other drug abuse professionals certified by more than 73 IC&RC member certification boards. IC&RC's mission is to establish, monitor, and advance reciprocal competency standards for alcohol and other drug abuse professionals and to support the member boards, which serve the public.

The purposes of IC&RC are:

• To advance international reciprocal standards in credentialing in the alcohol and other drug abuse treatment, prevention, and clinical supervision fields.

• To provide competency-based credentialing products which promote and sustain public protection.

• To develop partnerships with other organizations, governmental agencies, and groups concerned with the quality of care/services in the alcohol and other drug abuse profession.

• To foster an international organization based upon participatory government.

IC&RC/AODA Job Task Analysis Assessment Study (2008).[5] Over many years the Board Members of the IC&RC debated whether to re-validate the Case Presentation Method (CPM) or to eliminate the CPM as an evaluation requirement for initial certification or licensure as an alcohol and drug abuse counselor. The Executive Committee interviewed a number of companies that develop psychometric tests. IC&RC contracted with Schroeder Measurement Technologies (SMT) to develop, score, and administer the International Certification Examination for Alcohol and Other Drug Abuse Counselors. SMT is an established full-service international testing company serving the needs of licensing boards and credentialing agencies with a wide range of test development and computer-based administration services at testing centers.

---

[4] Taken, with permission, from the Candidate Guide for the International Certification Examination for Alcohol and Other Drug Counselors.
[5] Use of the information in this section is provided with permission of the IC&RC.

In the fall of 2007 the full Board voted to proceed with elimination of the oral examination or CPM and to incorporate the skills evaluated by the global criteria of the 12 Core Functions into a multiple-choice written examination.

The development of a valid examination for the IC&RC certification process begins with a clear and concise definition of the knowledges, skills, and abilities needed for competent job performance. Using interviews, surveys, observation, and group discussions, IC&RC worked with experts in the field of alcohol and other drug abuse to delineate critical job components.

A panel convened at SMT in Dunedin, FL to update the Knowledges, Skills and Attitudes (KSAs) for the Alcohol and Other Drug Abuse (AODA) credential. The Certified Alcohol and Other Drug Abuse Counselor Job Task Analysis Report 2008 identified eight performance domains for the alcohol and other drug abuse counselor. Within each performance domain are several identified tasks that provide the basis for questions in the revised examination. As of June 2008, the IC&RC written examination has a slightly different format than previous versions. Candidates for this revised written examination will find that the final 13 questions on the exam all relate to a single case study, a scenario, and then there are skills questions asked for the candidate to display competence. The following are the eight (8) performance domains:

Domain 1: Clinical Evaluation

Domain 2: Treatment Planning

Domain 3: Referral

Domain 4: Service Coordination

Domain 5: Counseling

Domain 6: Client, Family and Community Education

Domain 7: Documentation

Domain 8: Professional and Ethical Responsibilities

The tasks within each domain will be listed in the upcoming chapters for the 12 core functions, again, with permission of the IC&RC/AODA. It is appropriate for the entry-level substance abuse counselor to know as much about each core function **and** domain **and** to increase competency by understanding and studying other professional literature discussing KSAs related to a specific core function.

Structure for the Remaining Chapters. The next 12 chapters all have a common format. The IC&RC's core function definition is provided first followed by the definition of a similar performance domain or element within a performance domain from TAP 21. Then, there is a discussion of the core function. Next is a discussion of the core function from a client's point of view, then from a counselor's point of view. The global criteria for each of the core functions are discussed followed by a statement of the tasks for the related performance domain. Finally, in an effort to advance individual professional growth or to serve as assistance to instructors of counselor trainees, a number of assignments are provided. I invite instructors to share with me additional assignments they may have developed for their students.

A counselor seeking certification or licensure as a substance abuse counselor needs to be knowledgeable AND skillful in the role of being a professional substance abuse counselor. What makes this book a major contribution to the field is the discussion of global criteria, a set of criteria or skills to be displayed for demonstration of competence in each of the 12 core functions. Additionally, the statement of tasks identified in the performance domain related to the 12 core functions shows both knowledge AND skills. Competence is now assessed on the standardized written examination required by certification boards of the IC&RC. My hope is that this book increases the entry level competence of counselors and serves supervisors with additional understanding of the 12 core functions.

Chapter 2 - Screening

IC&RC defines screening as **the process by which a client is determined appropriate and eligible for admission to a particular program.**

TAP 21 includes the core function of screening in Domain I – CLINICAL EVALUATION.

TAP 21 Definition of Clinical Evaluation: The systematic approach to screening and assessment of individuals thought to have a substance use disorder, being considered for admission to addiction-related services, or presenting in a crisis situation.

Thus, TAP 21's definition of Clinical Evaluation includes three core functions: Screening; Assessment; and, Crisis Intervention.

Tap 21 identifies two Elements: Screening and Assessment. It does not specifically define an element for Crisis Intervention. It defines the element of screening as follows:

Element: Screening
Screening is the process by which the counselor, the client, and available significant others review the current situation, symptoms, and other available information to determine the most appropriate initial course of action, given the client's needs and characteristics and the available resources within the community.

It is appropriate for the entry-level substance abuse counselor to know as much about each core function and to increase competency by understanding and studying other professional literature discussing SKAs related to a specific core function.

The core function of screening requires the counselor to consider a number of factors before deciding whether or not to schedule the potential client for intake and admission to the program. Each alcohol and/or drug abuse program has requirements detailing factors that make a potential client appropriate and eligible. The following provides a number of the factors to be considered regarding appropriateness.

- The potential client needs to present **a possible alcohol or drug abuse problem** with the abused substance one that is treated in the program. It would be inappropriate to admit an alcoholic to a methadone maintenance program or to admit a cocaine abuser to an alcohol-only treatment program.

- The potential client's physical condition needs to be appropriate to the **level of care** provided within the program. Blindness, deafness, pregnancy and other physical handicaps might make a potential client inappropriate for a given program.

- A potential client needing detox would be inappropriate for an immediate outpatient program.

- A serious mental or medical illness may need to be addressed before alcohol and/or drug abuse treatment is initiated.

- The necessary outside supports and resources should exist for this potential client in order to facilitate the program treatment. A treatment program with a philosophy and focus on the family would be inappropriate for a runaway teenager with no family available or a homeless person with no family.

- The success or failure of previous treatment efforts may make a program appropriate now. It would usually be inappropriate to admit a client for their first treatment experience into a relapse program or to admit a potential client who left a detox program "Against Medical Advice" (AMA) to a halfway house.

- A potential client who is court-ordered to treatment should not be admitted to a completely voluntary program.

- A male should not be admitted to a program treating, for instance, pregnant females (also an eligibility factor).

The following provides a number of factors to be considered regarding eligibility.

- **Age of the client.** A 23-year-old male would not be eligible for admission to an adolescent program.

- **Gender.** A male would not be eligible for admission to a program treating only females.

- **Place of residence.** A resident of a neighboring county would not be eligible for admission to a program that is limited to treat only their own county residents.

- **Legal status.** A potential client would not be eligible for admission to an outpatient program when the person is currently (or about to be) incarcerated in prison.

- **Veteran status.** A non-veteran would not be eligible for admission to a VA hospital-based program.

- **Income level.** A potential client with no or little ability to pay for treatment would not be eligible for admission to a private practice outpatient program. A counselor would need to make an appropriate referral.

- **Referral source.** A potential client seeking treatment independently would not be eligible for admission to a program that only accepts referrals from a specific source such as the juvenile or adult probation office.

The core function of screening requires that the counselor or person doing the screening be skilled in knowing the signs and symptoms of substance abuse, know the eligibility requirements for the agency and what makes a potential client appropriate, be capable of ruling out potential clients with other or co-existing conditions, know the law, regulations and their agency's policies, be a skillful listener, and, be versed in keeping the necessary records for later use.

From the Client's Point of View

Screening is a counselor core function. However, in order to increase a counselor's skill in screening, taking the potential client's perspective will assist the counselor in greater understanding of the core function. The greatest majority of potential clients enter the screening process with an initial telephone call. Other entrance methods might be a walk-in, third-party contact., or, other treatment program seeking a lower or higher level of care. In many treatment programs the person conducting the initial screening is not the eventual counselor. In some programs a competent secretary or receptionist might do the initial screening. In other programs a counselor may be assigned the responsibilities of screening (and intake). Even if an applicant for certification does not perform the routine screening in their current agency, he or she must keep in mind that each certified counselor should maintain competency skills in screening.

From the client's perspective, something is happening in the client's life to either internally or externally motivate him or her to call or seek alcohol or drug abuse counseling or information. Internal motivation may come from the natural or logical consequences of substance use or abuse. A loved one may be abusing alcohol or drugs. A significant other may have given an ultimatum. An accident or DWI may have occurred. A person might say to him or herself, "It's about time I do something about my drinking."

External motivation is quite common motivational factor for seeking help in the alcohol and drug abuse field. The court systems of the country may require an evaluation and subsequent treatment. An employer may require treatment for the individual to keep a job. A spouse may seriously have the "bags packed" unless the individual agrees to get help.

A potential client's feelings may range from one extreme of hope and expectation to the other extreme of the severe negative emotions of anger and fear, or feelings may be neutral. As a counselor at the other end of a telephone, all the empathy and learned communication skills are needed to assist a client during the screening process. Connections begin with this initial contact. First impressions are important.

From the Counselor's Point of View

Screening as a process to determine whether a potential client is eligible and appropriate for admission to your program often becomes a routine matter — asking and answering questions. It is important at all times for the counselor to conduct him or herself in a professional manner. First impressions are very important. Presenting a positive image of one's self and one's agency is vital for survival as a treatment provider. Leaving a potential client with the impression of unconditional positive regard will both facilitate the client in continuing to seek treatment and enhance the beginning rapport necessary for effective confrontation and treatment later. In the business world it would be all about "customer service." The person conducting the screening needs to be the "Greatest Salesman in the World" and relate with empathy and clarity to each potential client.

Most often the initial screening is conducted over the telephone. A competent counselor will listen to what the potential client is saying, ask clarifying or probing questions, and, as appropriate, direct questions. A counselor needs to use appropriate diagnostic criteria to determine whether a potential client's alcohol or drug use constitutes abuse. Through the initial telephone interview a counselor solicits specific examples of how the potential client's use of alcohol or other drugs has become dysfunctional or a focus of concern for self or significant other(s).

Leslie, a counselor at a small outpatient clinic, receives a telephone call from a female caller who identifies herself as Victoria. "Is this the drug and alcohol clinic?" asks Victoria.

Leslie responds (direct question) "Yes, this is the Pathways to Change Counseling Center. We provide help for alcohol and drug problems. How can I help you?"

"Well, this is really hard for me (psychological sign). My husband says I drink too much (social sign), but he's such a nag. He says he's fed up with me (social sign). He says he's going to leave me (social sign)," says Victoria.

Leslie, demonstrating reflective listening skills, says, "Your husband is nagging you about your drinking. He's fed up and says he's leaving you."

Victoria simply responds, "Yea."

Leslie asks a probing question, "Tell me more about your drinking."

Victoria then responds, "My husband is a salesman. He's on the road a lot. I never know when he's coming home (social sign). It's so boring here staying at home all the time (psychological sign). I just drink in the afternoons while I watch the soaps. It helps me get through the day."

Leslie asks a direct question, "How much do you drink?"

"Oh, just two glasses of vodka. Just enough to get a buzz on (physiological sign)," says Victoria.

Leslie wonders how much vodka is in the glass. What is the size of the glass? Is it straight vodka? Perhaps Victoria has progressed to a reverse tolerance stage. Leslie asks two more direct questions, "How big is the glass?" and "About how much vodka do you go through in say one week?"

"Well, the glass is one of those water glasses and I go through, I don't know, two or three of those big bottles a week, I guess" (physiological sign).

Leslie can already evaluate that Victoria is most likely drinking abusively. Leslie asks another direct question, "Do you use any drugs?"

Victoria responds, "No. Just some Valium that my doctor prescribed for my nerves" (possible coexisting condition).

"How much of the Valium do you take?" asks Leslie (clarifying question).

"I hate taking pills. I only take some to help me sleep at night," says Victoria (physiological sign).

At this point Leslie changes direction of the interview and asks, "Tell me, Victoria, how do you feel about your husband telling you that you have a problem?" (probing question).

"I don't have a problem," Victoria says forcefully. "If he'd just pay me a little attention, I wouldn't have to drink at all" (psychological symptom).

This brief telephone interview demonstrates some of a counselor's skill in the area of screening, but does not address all of the global criteria of screening. Information obtained in the example above addresses signs and symptoms of substance use/abuse (Criterion 1) and a possible co-existing condition in the Valium/anxiety co-occurring condition (Criterion 4). This interview, as presented, does not address whether or not Victoria is appropriate and eligible for services (Criteria 2 and 3) at Leslie's agency, nor does it show whether or not Leslie followed applicable laws, regulations, and agency policies (Criterion 5).

Global Criteria

A critical component of the original IC&RC/CPM revision project was the defining of a set of global criteria for each core function. Think of global criteria as necessary skills needed by a counselor to perform the specific core function. The 2008 Job Task Analysis study identified both knowledge and skill tasks for entry level counselors. The global criteria and now the tasks identified in this study provide a unit of evaluation for determining an applicant's competence for certification or licensure as an alcohol and drug abuse counselor. What follows are the global criteria for screening and a discussion about demonstration of competence for the stated global criterion. At the end is a listing of tasks identified in the 2008 Job Task Analysis study that logically applies to the display of skills in the core function. In the following chapters this same format is followed.

1. Evaluate psychological, social and physiological signs and symptoms of alcohol and other drug use and abuse.

To be competent in this criterion, a counselor would need to know the psychological, social, and physiological signs and symptoms of alcohol and other drug use and abuse. The skill needed to demonstrate competence in this global criterion is the application of knowledge to the initial evaluation of the client seeking information or admission to a program. A counselor needs to recognize specific examples of the signs and symptoms of substance abuse. For example, psychological signs and symptoms of the effects of substance use or abuse might include depression, anxiety, low self-esteem, loneliness, and isolation. Social signs and symptoms might include parent/child conflict, spouse estrangement, loss or threat of loss of job, and legal charges such as DWI/DUI. Physiological signs and symptoms might include increased tolerance, liver problems, and withdrawal symptoms.

Remember, by definition, screening is the process by which the client is determined appropriate and eligible for admission to a particular program. While skill in evaluation is necessary in the screening process, the screening core function is different from the assessment core function. The depth of sophistication required in screening is less than that expected in assessment.

The skills needed to demonstrate competence in this global criterion are many and varied. A counselor's skill is an extension of knowledges gained in one's professional preparation. A competent counselor will need to be skillful and strategic in order to synthesize sparse information evaluating the psychological, social, and physiological signs and symptoms of alcohol and other drug use and abuse. A counselor does not have to be comprehensive in the initial evaluation during the screening process — that is the assessment core function. In screening, it is vital to evaluate enough information in order to decide if the potential client is a likely treatment candidate in your program.

2. Determine the client's eligibility for admission or referral.

To be competent in this criterion, a counselor would need to know and then apply the specific eligibility criteria of his or her program as determined by a program's focus, target population, and funding sources. Most, if not all, alcohol and drug abuse treatment services are licensed, usually by the state's department of health or a similar bureaucracy. Eligibility requirements are usually easily ascertained and include demographic variables such as age, gender, residence, ability to pay, and perhaps other variables. The key word to remember in this global criterion is demographics.

In Pathways to Change's program policy manual, eligibility requirements are rather broad. Individuals are eligible for services if they have an alcohol or drug abuse problem; are male or female and over the age of 18; and have the ability to pay for services whether with insurance or self-pay. In the example, Victoria initially met the broad eligibility requirements for possible admission to Pathways to Change.

Another way to look at eligibility is to ask oneself the question, "Could this client be admitted to my program?" In the next global criterion regarding appropriateness, a similar question to ask is, "Should this client be admitted to my program?"

3. Determine the client's appropriateness for admission or referral.

To be competent in this criterion, a counselor knows how to actively solicit information from the potential client. Or, a counselor can purposefully tell a potential client about the treatment program's modality, the level of care, and conditions needed for the person to be appropriate for admission to the program. Remember, level of care is the key point for determining appropriateness.

In the case of Leslie's program, a small outpatient clinic with broad criteria for appropriateness, Leslie might tell Victoria something like this:

"Victoria, before I can tell you whether I can help you here at Pathways to Change, I need to tell you a little about our program. We are a small outpatient-counseling center where people come usually one to three times a week for counseling. If you would need any kind of medical help, I would have to refer you to City Hospital until you could be seen again here. We are not able to see people who have any major medical or physical problems if those interfere with counseling, such as being deaf or not being physically capable of coming to our clinic. Would there be any reason why you might not be able to come in for an appointment?"

At the screening level, Leslie has determined that Victoria is appropriate for scheduling an appointment. Victoria is an adult female with a presenting alcohol and possibly prescription drug problem. The "bad nerves" would need to be further evaluated during the assessment process. Leslie's clinic can accept clients with some coexisting mental-health conditions; however, if evaluated as a primary problem, referral may be necessary. Victoria provided no information to indicate inappropriateness for admission to Leslie's program. The level of care available at Pathways to Change seems appropriate for Victoria's needs, at least at this point in time.

This criterion addresses whether a potential client is appropriate for admission to a program. Another way to look at this criterion is whether or not the potential client is appropriate for the "level of care" provided by your agency. In today's world of "managed-care," great emphasis is placed on level of care. Agencies and counselors need to justify why less restrictive means of treatment are inappropriate for a potential client. Would an inpatient or short-term residential program be more appropriate than an outpatient program or an intensive outpatient program? Is medical detox necessary? A counselor for certification needs to connect a potential client's initial presenting situation to the agency's level of care.

4. Identify any coexisting conditions (medical, psychiatric, physical, etc.) that indicate the need for additional professional assessment and/or services.

To be competent in this criterion, a counselor would need to recognize the limitations of one's background and training. Certification or licensure assumes that the counselor has enough educational background and training in order to be aware of the signs and symptoms for major coexisting conditions with substance abuse disorders. During the screening process a counselor must evaluate whether there are any obvious or known coexisting conditions that indicate the need for additional professional assessment and services. Depending upon the program, some conditions can be further assessed within the program. Others would need to be referred elsewhere. It is a counselor's ethical and professional responsibility to make a referral when the presenting picture indicates the presence of a coexisting condition for which the individual counselor or program is not equipped to treat.

This global criterion assumes that a counselor will have the skills to make this kind of initial evaluation. It is important to provide help to a potential client during the screening process to facilitate further evaluation and treatment. Should a coexisting condition be missed during screening, the assessment process is most likely to identify its presence and then an appropriate referral can be made. Thus, the criticality of "missing it" during the screening process is not great.

5. Adhere to applicable laws, regulations, and agency policies governing alcohol and other drug abuse services.

To be competent in this criterion, a counselor would need to know one's professional responsibilities, follow ethical requirements, and adhere at all times to applicable laws, regulations, and agency policies governing alcohol and other drug abuse services. The importance of this, I hope, has been drilled into each counselor during coursework and training. Adherence is not only important, but also critical, and a frequent skill to be demonstrated by a competent counselor.

In the core function of screening, a potential client is not yet a client; however, laws protecting clients' confidentiality are applicable. Additionally a U.S. applicant for certification should be aware of the Americans with Disabilities Act (ADA) and consequent requirements. Other laws addressing nondiscrimination must be adhered to. State laws may address issues such as IV drug use or infectious disease reporting. In Nebraska, and other states, pregnant females must be given priority in admission to treatment. Other countries may have their own laws and regulations that differ from what is common in the United States.

A counselor needs to be aware of applicable regulations and agency policies. For example, an Air Force alcohol and drug abuse counselor must comply with Air Force Instruction 44-121, which not only carries the "weight" of a regulation, but also is the Air Force's policy manual. A civilian counselor may have state or county regulations to comply with, and each agency should have a policy manual that covers screening policies and procedures. It is each counselor's responsibility to adhere to whatever agency policy applies in their treatment program.

In order to be competent in this global criterion of screening, a counselor would need to know what actions the counselor performs in order to comply with the applicable laws, regulations, or policies of the program. A program may have a checklist of prepared questions ready for a potential client prior to scheduling an intake appointment, or a specific form would need to be completed as part of the screening process. Knowledge of applicable laws, regulations, and agency policies must be practiced and demonstrated by the counselor's specific actions.

As I mentioned in Chapter 1, global criteria represent the skills considered important for a counselor to demonstrate competence in the 12 core functions. In the Certified Alcohol and Other Drug Abuse Counselor Job Task Analysis Report 2008 published by the IC&RC both knowledge AND skills were incorporated as tasks into 8 Performance Domains. It is important for the substance abuse counselor to be both knowledgeable AND skillful in his or her capacity as a substance abuse counselor. The core function of Screening is included in Domain 1, Clinical Evaluation and the following are the identified tasks appropriate to Screening in the domain of Clinical Evaluation.

Domain 1: Clinical Evaluation

- Demonstrate effective verbal and non-verbal communication to establish rapport.
- Discuss with the client the rationale, purpose, and procedures associated with the screening and assessment process to facilitate client understanding and cooperation.
- Assess client's current situation, including signs and symptoms of intoxication and withdrawal, by evaluating observed behavior and other available information to determine client's immediate needs.
- Administer the appropriate screening and assessment instruments specific to the client's age, developmental level, culture, and gender in order to obtain objective data to further assess client's current problems and needs.
- Obtain relevant history and related information from the client and other pertinent sources in order to establish eligibility and appropriateness to facilitate the assessment process.
- -Screen and assess for physical, medical and co-occurring disorders that might require additional assessment and referral.

The core function of Screening is also included, in part, in domain 4, Service Coordination and the following is the only screening-related task in the Domain of Service Coordination:

Domain 4: Service Coordination

- Prepare accurate and concise screening, intake, and assessment documents.

Assignments

1.   Interview a certified alcohol and drug abuse counselor. In one page or less describe how this professional conducts the core function of screening in their agency or practice.

2.   What are the necessary questions to ask during a good screening process? Itemize those questions. Design a one-page client screening form.

3.   List five possible coexisting conditions that an alcohol or drug abuse client might have.   Briefly describe the relationship of the coexisting condition to the presentation of substance abuse. Identify what additional professional assessment and/or services are needed.

4.   What federal and state laws and regulations apply to the screening process in your agency?

5.   What agency policies would you expect to have in a program policy manual governing the screening process?

6.   Review your agency's policies and procedures manual. Write a critique of how the agency addresses the five global criteria of screening.

7.   Write your own screening script for a potential client seeking treatment. Demonstrate your competence in screening by addressing within the script all five global criteria of screening.

8.   Role play conducting a screening with one other student. Seek feedback from others who listen to the role play.

As a bonus for professors, teachers, and instructors who train our future generation of professional alcohol and drug abuse counselors, I'm providing a lesson plan for the core function of screening. I wish I had lesson plans for each of the twelve core functions, but I do not. Please enjoy this bonus and, if you'd like, give me feed-back on it at jherdman@binary.net.

LESSON PLAN
12 CORE FUNCTIONS OF THE
SUBSTANCE ABUSE COUNSELOR
Core Function: Screening

SET: Think to yourself about how SCREENING is conducted in
                            your agency. Picture a person on the phone. What processes
                            do you go through to screen the client? List the questions
                            you might ask this person.

                            _____
                            _____
                            _____
                            _____
                            _____
                            _____
                            _____
                            _____

**OBJECTIVE/
MEANINGFUL
PURPOSE:**

Given an overview of Screening, TLWBA[6] to
 -- define the core function of screening.
 -- have knowledge of the five global criteria of screening.
 -- have an understanding of the five global criteria of screening, by explaining each global criterion in their own words and referencing their explanation to a case example.

What are your reasons for wanting to learn these global criteria?

_____

_____

_____

_____

_____

**INSTRUCTIONAL
INPUT:**

Read: Chapter 2 in the book by John W. Herdman, Ph.D., LADC, *Global Criteria: The 12 Core Functions of the Substance Abuse Counselor, Fifth Edition.*

View: The definition of Screening and the five global criteria of screening from the overhead or PowerPoint provided.

**CHECKING FOR
UNDERSTANDING:**

1. Define Screening.
2. What are the necessary questions to ask during the screening process that evaluate the psychological, social, and physiological signs and symptoms of alcohol and other drug use and abuse? Design a one-page client screening form.
3. How do you determine a client's appropriateness for admission to your agency or when to make a referral? List a number of factors that determine a client's appropriateness.
4. How do you determine a client's eligibility for admission to your agency or when to make a referral? List a number of factors that determine a client's eligibility.
5. List five possible coexisting conditions that an alcohol or drug abuse client might have. Briefly describe the relationship of the coexisting condition to the presentation of substance abuse. Identify what additional professional assessments and/or services are needed.
6. What federal and state laws, regulations, and agency policies apply to the screening process? Identify those that apply and discuss their applicability to the screening process.

---

[6] TLWBA = The Learner Will Be Able

GUIDED PRACTICE: Directions: Identify which global criteria is described by
                         each of the following statements:

                         a. Signs. symptoms of substance use/abuse
                         b. Appropriateness
                         c. Eligibility
                         d. Coexisting conditions
                         e. Laws, regulations, and agency policies

                         _____1. Age of the client
                         _____2. Veteran status
                         _____3. Civil Rights Act
                         _____4. Blackouts
                         _____5. Depression
                         _____6. Cirrhosis
                         _____7. Failure in outpatient services
                         _____8. Screening Form
                         _____9. Level of care
                         _____10. DWI

Check Yourself   1. c   6. d
                         2. c   7. b
                         3. e   8, e
                         4. a   9. b
                         5. d   10. a

CLOSURE: Imagine yourself in a room with other counselors taking a
                         written examination for certification or licensure for being an
                         alcohol and drug counselor. Recall the purpose of screening
                         and the process used with a client. Prepare an answer for
                         explaining the core function of screening and the skills
                         needed to display competence.

INDEPENDENT   Practice your answer to the above question in front of your
PRACTICE: peers and immediate supervisor. Ask each person for
                         feedback. Keep practicing.

Notes

Chapter 3 - Intake

IC&RC defines intake as **the administrative and initial assessment procedures for admission to a program.**

TAP 21 includes the core function of intake in Domain VII. DOCUMENTATION.

TAP 21 Definition of DOCUMENTATION: The recording of the screening and intake process, assessment, treatment plan, clinical reports, clinical progress notes, discharge summaries, and other client-related data.

Thus, TAP 21's definition of Documentation includes tasks of five (5) core functions: Screening; Intake, Assessment; Treatment Planning and, Reports and Record Keeping. TAP 21 does not specifically define a domain for Intake.

So often writers explain the intake process as if it were a continuation of screening or an in-depth assessment of a client. Intake is simpler than that. Intake is merely what the definition says, "The administrative and initial assessment procedures for admission to a program." It is all about the paperwork to get someone, the client, into treatment. The intake process, however, does not exist in a vacuum. In most if not all treatment programs, the process follows initial screening. Where initial screening tries to rule out potential clients as ineligible or inappropriate for a treatment program, initial assessment procedures during the intake process tries to "rule in" clients for treatment.

Intake does become an extension of screening that results in either the decision to admit an individual as a client (and the assessment and treatment process continues) or the individual is determined to be ineligible or inappropriate for the treatment program (in which case a referral to another program or professional resource may be made, if appropriate).

During intake various record forms are completed. Typically, the client and counselor fill out an admission or intake form, sign the HIPPA form, collect financial data, and sign a consent for treatment and any authorizations to release information that are identified as appropriate at this point in the process.

If the intake counselor is likely to be the primary counselor for the client, this is related to the client. If not, this is explained with enough detail to gain the client's understanding and establish expectations.

The intake counselor also will document the initial assessment in accordance with agency policy in enough detail to assist a subsequent and more comprehensive assessment. This documentation becomes part of the client record.

In many substance abuse treatment facilities, the next core function — the orientation of the client by a counselor — also is completed during the intake session. If not then, an additional appointment is made to orient the client and continue the assessment process.

From the Client's Point of View

Typically the first face-to-face meeting between a client and a treatment provider occurs during the intake process. In many programs the person doing the intake will be the counselor who will subsequently provide treatment. In other programs a different person is assigned to do the intake and the one who conducts the treatment is the primary counselor.

There are a number of psychological factors affecting clients immediately prior to their entering the intake process. For a moment imagine yourself at home getting ready to go to an appointment where you will have to discuss problems of a personal nature. The feelings you might expect to have are likely to be some degree of unpleasantness. Anticipatory anxiety is both common and expected. More severe anxiety may actually stop you from keeping the appointment and would be a significant mental health symptom. For those addicted to their drug of choice, there may already be withdrawal symptoms present. Anger at a third party for "making you go" is not uncommon.

Now imagine yourself being a naïve first-time client whose only experiences with the "helping professions" has been a periodic physical examination. You most likely don't know what to expect once you are in the waiting room. You may still be experiencing some anxiety and apprehension. You may have some physiological symptoms, i.e., sweaty hands, churning stomach, or even colitis. You are greeted by the intake counselor and go with him or her to a small private room or an office unlike any medical examining room you have ever seen. You still don't know what to expect. Anxiety continues.

Imagine yourself now being a DWI offender who is being sent to a treatment program for an evaluation. You don't think you have a problem. You feel angry and upset. The appointment is an inconvenience and a "waste of your time." You carry this resentment with you to the appointment and into the intake interview.

As a third example, imagine yourself being an experienced client. You may have been in mental health or pastoral counseling before or have had previous alcohol or drug abuse treatment and are now in relapse. You know what to expect. There are likely to be no surprises. Although you are not likely to be perfectly calm about it, you likely will have less anticipatory anxiety, fear, or anger.

From the Counselor's Point of View

As an intake counselor, it is important to be aware of what your client may be feeling. The screening information may give you some indication of the client's emotional status, but not always. As a counselor, your therapeutic relationship begins with greeting the client. First impressions are important. An intake counselor needs to develop skills at assessing the client's initial feelings by evaluating their body language, verbal interaction, and communication. When you recognize the emotions of the client you are better able to manage your relationship and interaction with him or her.

The intake process is the administrative and initial assessment procedures for program admission. Your role is to determine that this particular individual is indeed eligible and appropriate for your program. It typically involves a lot of paperwork. All clients go through some sort of intake process no matter what kind of treatment program they are being considered for. The amount of intake paperwork will vary depending upon the type of program, its focus, its needs and its philosophy.

Counselors often do not like the paperwork aspect of the job. For some, the intake is too routine. It is important to remember that this first appointment is not likely to be routine for the client. The client is dealing with a lot of emotions. Oftentimes a client would also rather skip the paperwork and get right to the issues. The client is often hurting and wants the pain to stop. It is the counselor's responsibility to balance the need to complete paperwork with establishing the initial therapeutic relationship. Failure to adequately complete required paperwork may leave the counselor and agency open to litigation should a client believe he or she were wronged in some way.

In many treatment programs the functions of intake, orientation, and assessment are often part of the first appointment. Creating a balance of paperwork, listening to the client, and doing an assessment should contribute to reducing the anxiety of the client, establishing initial rapport, and facilitating the assessment and future treatment process.

In other treatment programs, intake alone, or intake and orientation, are completed during the first appointment. The more comprehensive assessment process is scheduled for the second appointment.

In my own clinic, we do a great number of chemical dependency assessments for attorneys, the court and Probation. The assessment determines a level of care recommendation and then a referral to an appropriate treatment agency. In this case, the assessment is already done before intake.

The definition of intake refers to that process of "initial assessment for admission to a program." This refers to the intake counselor being skillful at evaluating and determining that the potential client is, indeed, eligible and appropriate for the treatment program. The purpose of screening is to rule out individuals who would be ineligible or inappropriate for admission. The task of intake is to rule in the individual as eligible and also appropriate for admission with sufficient documentation to justify a decision about admission and to facilitate further evaluation and treatment if that should be the case.

Global Criteria

6. Complete required documents for admission to the program.

In order to be competent in this global criterion a counselor would need to:

- Be aware of what forms are required within the agency in order to admit an individual as a client;

- know the "what" and the "how" of the admission activity; and,
- know that the information is to be written down and the documents are adequately completed for admission to the program.

A counselor should remember that this criterion is related to administrative documentation. Forms may include demographic information; a signed consent for treatment; financial responsibility forms, and other federal, state or agency required forms.

In 2003 the United States government enacted the Health Information Protection and Portability Act, know as HIPAA. This law has created the need for counselors and agencies to provide a "Notice" of the act and its meaning to all clients and to have the client sign acknowledgement of having been given the HIPAA notice. This is now a required document and completing this form in this global criterion is appropriate.

7. Complete required documents for program eligibility and appropriateness.

In order to be competent in this global criterion a counselor would need to:

- Know what forms are required within the agency in order to document a client's eligibility and appropriateness for admission to the program; and
- know that information is written down and completed, documenting the client's eligibility and appropriateness for the program.

A counselor should remember that this criterion relates to documenting eligibility and appropriateness. Demographic information may document some of this; other forms may be insurance information forms, pay statements, results from initial assessment tools such as the CAGE or Michigan Alcoholism Screening Test (MAST) or information documented during the screening process.

8. Obtain appropriately signed consents when soliciting from or providing information to outside sources to protect client confidentiality and rights.

In order to be competent in this global criterion a counselor would need to:

- Have knowledge and understanding of the need for a client signing a form that allows the counselor to obtain confidential information from another source or to be able to release confidential information from the counselor to a third-party; and,
- Facilitate the client signing authorization(s) to release information documenting to whom, and why. If no releases are signed during the intake process, the counselor would need to understand why there was no need to obtain information from outside sources or to release information to a third party.

With the enactment of HIPPA, the term "authorization(s)" appears to be the politically correct term to identify what for years was known as "release" or "releases." Actually, authorization does appear more appropriate as the client is authorizing the counselor or agency to release information.

As I mentioned in Chapter 1, global criteria represent the skills considered important for a counselor to demonstrate competence in the 12 core functions. In the Certified Alcohol and Other Drug Abuse Counselor Job Task Analysis Report 2008 published by the IC&RC both knowledge AND skills were incorporated as tasks into 8 Performance Domains. It is important for the substance abuse counselor to be both knowledgeable AND skillful in his or her capacity as a substance abuse counselor. The core function of Intake is included, in part, in Domain 4, Service Coordination and the following is the only intake-related task in the Domain of Service Coordination:

Domain 4: Service Coordination

- Prepare accurate and concise screening, intake, and assessment documents.

Assignments

1. Design your own checklist to be used for admitting a client to your program.

2. Design your own form that documents a client's eligibility and appropriateness for your program.

3. Design a HIPPA compliant authorization form that adheres to applicable laws, regulations, and agency policies for releasing client information.

4. Write a one-paragraph script to reflect how you would explain the need for administrative paperwork to a client.

5. Write a script that explains to a client both the need to obtain confidential information from another source and to release confidential information to another third party.

6. Describe how would you deal with a client who is angry and hostile during the intake process?

7. A potential client comes into your agency for the initial intake. In your evaluation the client is not appropriate for your program. Discuss three possible reasons why an individual might not be appropriate; how you would go about referring the individual, if appropriate; and, write a script for referring an individual to another treatment resource.

8. Identify and list the various forms used in the intake process.

9. Sit down with another student and role play conducting an intake process and listen to feedback from those observing.

Notes

Chapter 4 - Orientation

IC&RC defines Orientation as **describing to the client the general nature and goals of the program; the rules governing client conduct and infractions that can lead to disciplinary action or discharge from the program, the hours during which services are available; the treatment costs that are to be borne by the client, if any; and the client's rights.**

TAP 21 does not address a Domain of Orientation.

While the orientation function is mostly administrative, to forget the therapeutic impact of a good orientation would be unfortunate. The core function of orientation varies greatly from treatment setting to treatment setting, and from provider to provider. The orientation follows the screening and intake functions, and logically occurs before any treatment is provided. Although orientation is usually done individually, it also may be done in a family or in a group setting. In a formal setting, a multidisciplinary team may inform the client of the multitude of services that are available. In a more informal setting, one counselor may do it all.

From the Client's Point of View

Most clients expect to be told what is required of them early in the treatment process. A client should not experience any surprise when a counselor announces that, "Now I'd like to tell you about our program." The orientation process should help to reduce client anxiety, apprehension, and answer the client's important questions.

From the Counselor's Point of View

The orientation process is usually conducted at the time of intake or shortly thereafter. Once a client has been screened as eligible and appropriate and the intake information (including the initial assessment and completion of forms) agrees with the screening information, then the counselor is obligated to inform the client about the treatment program.

To inadequately inform a client of the rules that may result in the client's discharge from the program or service, the client's financial obligations, and the client's rights would be unprofessional, unethical, and open a counselor and the treatment agency to civil liability. There is precedence for civil and professional charges when such information is not adequately provided to a client. A counselor must keep in mind that his or her behavior may, at any time, be questioned by a client; and may involve attorneys and the courts. Counselor accountability is more often called into question today than at anytime in the past. You don't want to be in a position of saying, "I should have explained that to you".

The adequate orientation of a client to a treatment program should involve oral and written communication. This should be done while the counselor continues to establish rapport using motivational interviewing techniques, empathy and listening skills. The counselor should orally communicate the general nature and goals of the treatment program, the rules governing conduct and the consequences for violating these rules (including discharge from the treatment program), the general schedule for treatment; financial obligations, and a general explanation of client rights. It is also important that a client receives a copy of the orientation materials and signs an acknowledgment that he or she has been "oriented" to the treatment program. These documents should become a part of the client's records. Should there ever be an internal or external review of whether a client was adequately oriented, a signature will help assure others that the counselor performed the orientation function as required by the program.

Global Criteria

9. Provide an overview to the client by describing program goals and objectives for client care.

To be competent in this criterion, a counselor understands the importance of telling a client about the treatment program's goals and objectives. A counselor should not confuse "program goals and objectives for client care" with the client's goals and objectives detailed in the treatment plan. A counselor in an inpatient program for example, would state to a client that one goal of this treatment program is abstinence from alcohol and other mind-altering drugs. The client also would be told that this goal will be addressed by a combination of client education and with individual and group counseling while in active inpatient treatment. Following inpatient treatment the client would receive further assistance through counseling and their attendance in a self-help support group. Failure to relate the program goals and objectives to a client is a most frequent mistake for entry-level counselors.

Today, many agencies and programs have vision and mission statements. Think of these as reflecting the goals and objectives of the program. You may need to translate the vision and mission to reflect goals and objectives, but as you become more familiar with this criterion, I have confidence that you will be able to do so.

As an example of program goals and objectives, let me share with you what Leslie tells Amanda at Pathways to Change, an outpatient program.

"Amanda, the program goal here at Pathways to Change is the same for everyone. Our goal is to help our clients stay out of trouble with the law, with their significant others and on the job. We do this by teaching solution-focused problem solving skills or cognitive-behavioral skills during individual, group and family sessions."

Notice that the program goal is the same for everyone. As an outpatient program, clients include those who abuse and those who are substance dependent. Programs that admit substance dependent individuals often have a program goal of abstinence from all mind-altering substances. Each program or agency sets its own program goals and objectives appropriate for their vision and mission.

10. Provide an overview to the client by describing program rules, and client obligations and rights.

To be competent in this criterion, a counselor would need to know and explain specific program rules, specific client obligations, and give examples of client rights to each client.

Examples of program rules might include abstinence (i.e., no drinking or drugging prior to a scheduled treatment session; while in treatment), no physical aggression, no firearms allowed on the premise, and lights must be out by 11:00 p.m.

Examples of client obligations might include the obligations to keep all scheduled appointments or to call giving a 24-hour notice if unable to keep an appointment; to pay for services rendered; and, to keep information heard in group sessions confidential. It is sometimes good to think of client obligations as client responsibilities.

All clients have rights. In all treatment programs a client has the right to professional treatment as well as the right to confidentiality, although within the limits of the agency, e.g., the military. All treatment programs have statements of client rights and you, as a counselor, should ask each client to sign that he or she has received information about their rights.

11. Provide an overview to the client of program operations.

To be competent in this criterion, a counselor would need to answer the question, "How does this program work?" In providing an answer, the competent counselor would give an overview of the program and how the program operates. This would include but not be limited to the hours of operation, general schedule, phone numbers, type and frequency of appointments, and emergency access information. In a short-term residential treatment program, a counselor might describe a "typical day" to the client or provide a published weekly schedule. In an outpatient program the counselor might describe the agency's usual scheduling and other details to ensure smooth and effective treatment.

As I mentioned in Chapter 1, global criteria represent the skills considered important for a counselor to demonstrate competence in the 12 core functions. In the Certified Alcohol and Other Drug Abuse Counselor Job Task Analysis Report 2008 published by the IC&RC both knowledge AND skills were incorporated as tasks into 8 Performance Domains. It is important for the substance abuse counselor to be both knowledgeable AND skillful in his or her capacity as a substance abuse counselor. The core function of Orientation is not specifically related to any of the 8 Performance Domains, but is subsumed in the domain of Professional Responsibilities.

Assignments

1. Develop your own script for explaining to a client the program goals and objectives for each of the following:

    a. an inpatient program,

    b. a short-term residential program,

    c. an intensive outpatient program,

    d. an outpatient program,

    e. a detoxification program,

    f. A sober-living program.

2. Develop your own script for explaining to a client the program rules, as well as the client's obligations and rights for each of the following:

    a. an inpatient program,

    b. a short-term residential program,

    c. an intensive outpatient program,

    d. an outpatient program

    e. a detoxification program,

    f. a sober-living program.

3. Develop your own script for explaining to a client the program operations for each of the following:

    a. an inpatient program,

    b. a short-term residential program,

    c. an intensive outpatient program,

    d. an outpatient program

    e. a detoxification program,

    f. a sober-living program.

4. Compare and contrast how a professional in an allied field orients a client to his or her services.

5.   Obtain a copy of your agency's orientation forms. Critique these forms. How could you change/improve them?

6.   Role play an orientation session with another student and listen to feedback from those observing.

Notes

Chapter 5 - Assessment

IC&RC defines Assessment as **those procedures by which a counselor/program identifies and evaluates an individual's strengths, weaknesses, problems, and needs for the development of the treatment plan.**

TAP 21 includes the core function of Assessment in Domain I – CLINICAL EVALUATION.

TAP 21 Definition of Assessment: Assessment is an ongoing process through which the counselor collaborates with the client and others to gather and interpret information necessary for planning treatment and evaluating client progress.

The assessment process begins with the first contact during screening and is ongoing throughout the entire treatment experience. The word "procedures" indicates that the counselor does more than one "thing" to help in first identifying then evaluating a client's strengths, weaknesses, problems, and needs. Once the identification and evaluation is complete, the counselor then develops a treatment plan.

Why conduct an assessment of a client? A counselor does this so that an accurate diagnosis can be established. An accurate diagnosis then leads to the "prescription" of an appropriate treatment. Failure to make a valid assessment before providing therapy is like a medical doctor prescribing medication before asking a patient, "What's wrong?" or "Where does it hurt?" In other words it is like "Putting the cart before the horse."

Providing a valid assessment is the basis for a sound treatment program and can be reasonably compared to a physician making a valid diagnosis. Considerable harm can come to a client at the hands of an incompetent counselor doing an assessment. For example, at its worst, failing to assess suicidality could result in direct harm to the client and possible litigation against the counselor or agency. Also harmful is the failure to assess critical issues that, left unaddressed, would lead to relapse and treatment failure.

As a Clinical Director of a substance abuse treatment program I've seen quite a number of "mistakes" in other counselor's assessment reports. For example, I received a report from one master's level counselor who diagnosed a client with a DSM-IV diagnosis of cannabis abuse. In my intake with this client I learned that he had not used marijuana for 17 years, not since he was discharged from military service. Clearly, he no longer met DSM-IV criteria for the condition of cannabis abuse. Another common error made by many counselors is to provide a DSM-IV code of V71.09, especially on Axis II. This code indicates that there is no diagnosis or condition on Axis II. Unless a counselor is also certified or licensed to make such diagnoses, it is unethical to indicate that no diagnosis exists when such ability to diagnose is outside most alcohol and drug abuse counselors scope of practice. An appropriate code would be 799.9 which indicates the counselor does not know if an Axis II diagnosis is present or not and that someone with the appropriate credentials should consider the data or conduct additional assessment in order to diagnosis whether an Axis diagnosis exists or not.

Although assessment is an ongoing process, it is usually emphasized early in the treatment experience. Following admission, intake and orientation, a counselor or multidisciplinary team conducts an assessment of the individual client. The assessment can either be extensive and formal or limited and informal. However most, if not all, licensed treatment facilities are required in each case to document how the assessment is conducted. Facility licensing standards, and thus facility policies and procedures, usually detail the areas that must be assessed. A bio-psycho-social assessment is often a term used to describe this assessment. All tests, notes, and written assessments become part of the client record.

The counselor should assess a client in all "major" life areas, i.e., substance abuse history, psychological history and current functioning, educational history, vocational history, financial status, legal history, social history, spirituality, and physical health history including current medications and treatment history. Most of this "history" is gathered using interview techniques and completion of various locally prepared "psychosocial history" forms. If the treatment team includes a psychologist, then personality inventories, projective techniques, and clinical interviews are sometimes administered in order to assess current psychological functioning and identify the presence (or absence) of a "dual diagnosis" or "dual disorder" or co-occurring disorder.

While gathering information takes a certain amount of skill, the key to performing this core function competently is on the higher level ability of evaluating and synthesizing the client's information. The assessment process is much like detective work. Evaluation challenges the counselor to be not only knowledgeable about alcohol and drug abuse, but also to assess the extent to which a client's alcohol or drug use has interfered with the client's life functioning and activities of daily living (ADLs). A counselor needs to know how to make sense of the information gathered. At times the counselor must make sense of nonsense and make note of inconsistencies and contradicition. In the assessment process, answers to a counselor's questions may only become available as denial is broken through or as significant others become further involved in the treatment process.

During the assessment stage, a client's use and abuse of alcohol or other drugs may be his or her most obvious "problem" with the obvious "need" to stop using or abusing the substance. The assessment process also requires that a counselor identify and evaluate a client's strengths and weaknesses. This aspect of assessment is frequently overlooked or minimized in counselor training and supervision since the emphasis is on the client's presenting problems and needs.

From the Client's Point of View

For a client, assessment is one of those expected events that occur as part of a treatment program. Most clients expect helping professionals and "bureaucracies" to ask them a lot of diagnostic questions such as, "How much do you drink?" "For how long?" While they will be anxious for the "real treatment" to begin, they will experience some discomfort in being asked personal questions, especially if they perceive the questions as unrelated to drug and/or alcohol history. They will be uncomfortable with questions not obviously related to drinking or drugging, such as their sexual and relationship behavior and history. The assessing counselor should always be aware that the greater the perceived invasion of privacy, the greater the chance that the client will engage in denial and avoidance. Being skillful in Motivational Interviewing techniques greatly facilitates the counselor gaining meaningful assessment data.

From the Counselor's Point of View

In the assessment process, empathy for the client's perspective is critical for both establishing rapport and the subsequent therapeutic relationship. Clients will all behave somewhat differently. Some will be open and honest; others defensive and in denial. Some clients will be in such distress that their only thoughts are related to making their pain stop. Others in less distress will wish the counseling to begin, not being aware of the need for a complete assessment of their life. It is the competent counselor's responsibility to explain the need for assessment, what will be done in conducting the assessment, and what the counselor as well as the client can learn as a result of the assessment. The initial result of the assessment will be a treatment "prescription," i.e., the treatment plan. Only if the client is presenting in a crisis should the assessment process be deferred.

Assessment includes both interview techniques for both the client and significant others, and written questionnaires and tests. The assessment should not be a "pen and paper exercise" alone. Although time and counselor effort can be saved by having a client independently complete various questionnaires and tests, a counselor should not strictly rely on this. A counselor is trained to understand and evaluate a client's difficulty in being truthful and forthright. In the interview a counselor is more likely to detect the client's denial system and rationalization and be able to roll with client resistance.

Accurate assessment takes time. An entire assessment is not likely to be completed in one 50-minute session. Depending on the treatment setting and the skill and training of the counselor doing the assessment, this function is likely to take two or three sessions with changes made to the treatment plan (or prescription) as new information is obtained and evaluated.

Some counselors begin client education with assessment while other counselors begin the counseling process during the assessment process. A counselor should display appropriate empathy along with the communication skills to facilitate the establishment of rapport. However, education and counseling are more appropriately performed after the counselor evaluates the client comprehensively and has a focus or plan for treatment. Remember, providing education and doing counseling before a complete assessment is much like a medical doctor giving out educational material or prescribing medication prior to making the final diagnosis.

Global Criteria

12. Explain to the client the rationale for the use of assessment techniques in order to facilitate understanding.

To be competent in this criterion, a counselor will need to understand and communicate the rationale for the various aspects of the assessment to the client. In the explanation the counselor must answer clearly the following questions:

"What is assessment?"

"How are we (the counselor and client) going to go about doing the assessment?"

"Why do we have to do an assessment?"

"How long will it take?"

"What will happen after we do the assessment?"

"Who will have access to the assessment results?"

Understanding and implementing this criterion "sets the stage" for all aspects of the assessment process.

13. Gather relevant history from the client including but not limited to alcohol and other drug abuse using appropriate interview techniques.

To be competent in this criterion, a counselor will need to be skillful in basic interview techniques and in using the clinical interview as a procedure to identify a client's strengths, weaknesses, problems and needs. A counselor interviews and gathers information from the client about alcohol and drug use and then also gathers information about other bio-psycho-social aspects of the client with specific attention to how alcohol or drug use has impacted those areas of the client's life. For example, Leslie learned in the interview with Victoria that she was drinking two to three bottles of alcohol a week and was using Xanax for "bad nerves." Family history shows that Victoria's mother was probably an alcoholic and that she had been physically abused by her. Additionally, Leslie learned that Victoria married at an early age in order to escape her unhealthy home situation.

I have learned over the years of doing workshops on the core functions and global criteria that this criterion is sometimes problematic for students. The criterion requires "appropriate interview techniques." Knowing more than one technique is necessary to be competent. The difficulty some students have is in narrowly thinking that an interview is the one and only technique possible. There are structured interview techniques available in the field and agencies often have a "bio-psycho-social" assessment form. Clients can complete these as a structured interview technique and then further informal questioning or interviewing based upon the structured responses to the forms is an additional technique. I know one counselor that uses a different color of ink to comment on client responses and to increase clarity of an issue. An excellent example of a structured interview technique that includes the opportunity for probing questions is the Addiction Severity Index (ASI).

14. Identify methods and procedures for obtaining corroborative information from significant secondary sources regarding the client's alcohol and other drug abuse and psychosocial history.

To be competent in this criterion, a counselor needs to be aware of the benefits of obtaining corroborative information and the methods or means for how information is obtained from important secondary sources. This will necessitate being aware of client confidentiality rights and knowing the procedure for obtaining the information that protects the client's rights. For example, Leslie asked Victoria's permission to meet with her traveling salesman husband. Since Victoria agreed, an authorization for release of information was explained and signed. Leslie learned from Victoria's husband that he had left her on two occasions, both times following severe arguments when Victoria was drunk. On one occasion while he was on the road he feared for their kid's safety and he reported her to the Children and Youth Services in his county. He confirmed that he, too, thought that Victoria's mother was an alcoholic.

15. Select appropriate assessment tools.

In addition to the clinical interview, a competent counselor will need to be skillful in the selection and use of various assessment tools in order to assess a client. Examples of tools include the Alcohol Severity Index (ASI), the Michigan Alcohol Screening Test (MAST), the Mortimer-Filkins, the Alcohol Expectancy Questionnaire (AEQ), the Alcohol Use Inventory (AUI), the Self-Administered Alcoholism Screening Test (SAAST), the Substance Abuse Subtle Screening Inventory (SASSI), the Alcohol Dependence Scale (ADS), and other similar tools. Other members of the treatment team, such as psychologists, also use tools like the Minnesota Multiphasic Personality Inventory-2 (MMPI-2) or the MacAndrews Scale which is a 49-item subscale of the MMPI-2, the Millon Clinical Multiaxial Inventory-III (MCMI-III), or other psychological measures, including projective tests. A competent alcohol and drug abuse counselor needs to have an understanding of assessment tools used to evaluate a client. A counselor should have skill in evaluating the results of their own assessment tools and know the implications of assessment results from other members of the multidisciplinary treatment team. Following the comprehensive assessment, the counselor is responsible for using assessment results to develop a treatment plan.

16. Develop a diagnostic evaluation of the client's substance abuse and any coexisting conditions based on the results of all assessments in order to provide an integrated approach to treatment planning based on the client's strengths, weaknesses, and identified problems and needs.

To be competent in this criterion, a counselor needs to "make sense" of the gathered assessment information. Diagnostic evaluations are usually written documents and can range in length from one paragraph to multiple pages. The competent counselor synthesizes the information gathered and does not merely regurgitate a series of "facts" obtained. The counselor evaluates the information and relates the information directly or indirectly to the client's presenting problem or problems. Not only does the counselor make sense of the information he or she obtained during the assessment process, but also the information obtained by other members of the treatment team. The counselor will need to knowledgeably relate the client's alcohol or other drug abuse problem to any other coexisting conditions.

In the written assessment report there is usually a summary of the pertinent findings and a logical discussion of how an individual meets the criteria of DSM-IV for a particular substance abuse diagnosis. Follow this with the identification of strengths, weaknesses, problems and needs of the client. Then, the counselor provides a list of appropriate recommendations that logically flow from the assessment data and will address the client's identified strengths, weakness, problems and needs.

The diagnostic evaluation is the starting point for the development of the client's treatment plan. Within the assessment report a counselor specifies a client's strengths and weaknesses in a comprehensive manner so that any member of the treatment team or future referral source would have a clear picture of the client. Detailing the client's problems and needs is necessary in order to design intervention and treatment activities focused on the client's problem or problems.

As I mentioned in Chapter 1, global criteria represent the skills considered important for a counselor to demonstrate competence in the 12 core functions. In the Certified Alcohol and Other Drug Abuse Counselor Job Task Analysis Report 2008 published by the IC&RC both knowledge AND skills were incorporated as tasks into 8 Performance Domains. It is important for the substance abuse counselor to be both knowledgeable AND skillful in his or her capacity as a substance abuse counselor. The core function of Assessment is included in Domain 1, Clinical Evaluation and the following are the tasks in the Domain of Clinical Evaluation:

Domain 1: Clinical Evaluation

- Demonstrate effective verbal and non-verbal communication to establish rapport.
- Discuss with the client the rationale, purpose, and procedures associated with the screening and assessment process to facilitate client understanding and cooperation.

- Assess client's current situation, including signs and symptoms of intoxication and withdrawal, by evaluating observed behavior and other available information to determine client's immediate needs.
- Administer the appropriate screening and assessment instruments specific to the client's age, developmental level, culture, and gender in order to obtain objective data to further assess client's current problems and needs.
- Obtain relevant history and related information from the client and other pertinent sources in order to establish eligibility and appropriateness to facilitate the assessment process.
- Screen and assess for physical, medical and co-occurring disorders that might require additional assessment and referral.
- Interpret results of data in order to integrate all available information, formulate diagnostic impressions, and determine an appropriate course of action.
- Develop a written summary of the results of the assessment in order to document and support the diagnostic impressions and treatment recommendations.

Assignments

1.   Prepare a script for explaining the assessment process to a client.

2.   What signs and symptoms of alcohol use and/or abuse would you expect to see if the client you are assessing is a "problem drinker"?

3.   What signs and symptoms of alcohol use and/or abuse would you expect to see if the client you are assessing is diagnosed as an "alcohol or other drug abuser?"

4.   What signs and symptoms of alcohol use and/or abuse would you expect to see if the client you are assessing is diagnosed as "alcohol or other drug dependent?"

5.   What factors are important to consider in the differential diagnosis of bipolar disorder-manic and the use and/or abuse of stimulant drugs?

6.   What factors are important to consider in the differential diagnosis of bipolar disorder-depressive and the use and/or abuse of depressive drugs, including alcohol?

7.   Identify at least six assessment tools used by alcohol and drug abuse counselors and prepare a description of each.

8.   Identify at least six assessment tools used by other professionals of the treatment team and prepare a description of each.

9.   Develop a "boiler-plate" format for a comprehensive assessment of a client.

10. Conduct an assessment of a friend or classmate regarding their real or made-up experiences with substance use. Keep the person's anonymity. Prepare a written report of your assessment

Notes

Chapter 6 - Treatment Planning

IC&RC defines Treatment Planning as **the process in which the counselor and the client identify and rank problems needing resolution, establish agreed upon immediate and long-term goals, and decide on the treatment methods and resources to be used.**

TAP 21 includes the core function of TREATMENT PLANNING in Domain II – Treatment Planning.

TAP 21 Definition of TREATMENT PLANNING: A collaborative process in which professionals and the client develop a written document that identifies important treatment goals; describes measurable, time-sensitive action steps toward achieving those goals with expected outcomes; and reflects a verbal agreement between a counselor and client.

At a minimum an individualized treatment plan addresses the identified substance use disorder(s), as well as issues related to treatment progress, including relationships with family and significant others, potential mental conditions, employment, education, spirituality, health concerns, and social and legal needs.

"Failing to plan is planning to fail" is not only an appropriate saying for the counselor's approach to treatment planning, but it is also appropriate for the counselor's approach to all of the counselor core functions. If done well, treatment planning relates the client's strengths and weaknesses to the client's problems and needs.

Treatment planning logically occurs after the assessment process. The plan is based on the diagnostic evaluation of the client's strengths and weaknesses as well as the client's problems and needs. Both the counselor and client develop this plan. The outcome of treatment planning provides coherence and guidance for all future administrative and therapeutic activities. Treatment planning serves as both an administrative requirement and therapeutic function.

An administrative requirement of all licensed treatment facilities is to have an individualized treatment plan for each client. An agency's policy and procedures manual should detail the specific format of the plan and require when and how the plan should be reviewed and modified (if necessary). The plan is the protocol designed to reduce or eliminate the client's problems with alcohol or other drug use, and any coexisting problems identified as appropriate for treatment.

As a therapeutic function, the treatment plan identifies for the client and the counselor the problem statements, goals, and, objectives/activities to be addressed during treatment. To be successful the counselor needs to have a clear understanding of what the program proposes to accomplish with the client, i.e., the program goals and objectives. Additionally, the counselor needs to know client's goals and objectives and then plan the therapeutic interventions that will achieve these goals, i.e., the individualized treatment plan.

The counselor will find that a clear conceptualization of the treatment plan will be inordinately helpful if a standardized format is used. Although you or your agency may have a defined format for the treatment plan, the following is an example of an administrative framework for organizing a client's treatment linking

- Problem statement

- Goals

- Objectives

Within this framework, all planned intervention activities should be appropriate for the client's problem, and the outcomes should be derived from a statement of these problems and the selected interventions.

Some counselors mistakenly start with thinking about the nature of the intervention to be used with a client instead of identifying the client's problem that should be addressed. This is like a doctor prescribing medicine before he or she has made a diagnosis.

The framework for an effective treatment plan prescribes three components and addresses the following:

1. **Problem(s) Statement:** The first step for the treatment plan is to specify the problem(s) that the treatment program intends to address based on the preceding assessment. A problem statement can be defined as a negative condition for the client upon which treatment goals and objectives are to be based. Each problem statement will be addressed by the yet to be identified goals and corresponding objectives.

    Example: This individual has a history of abusing stimulant type drugs during stressful situations and for leisure activities, thus he is experiencing financial, legal and familial difficulties.

2. **Goals:** These are the expected results or conditions stated in relatively broad terms and based on an identified problem(s). The goal is often the inverse of the problem statement leading to positive outcome.

    An overall goal for a client might be abstinence from all mind-altering substances. The specified problems describe the conditions that prevent the realization of this goal. A counselor might ask oneself, "What factors, what behaviors, and what conditions prevent the realization of abstinence?" One answer might be that all high-risk behaviors and all high-risk genetic and environmental conditions that impede abstinence are problems. Yet this answer is not useful in the development of a client's treatment plan.

A counselor needs to be more specific and identify only those behaviors and conditions the counselor intends to address. Moreover, the behaviors and conditions that are selected by the counselor and client must be amenable to change. For example, being economically disadvantaged may be a risk factor for substance abuse but unless the counselor intends to somehow provide sufficiently more money for the client this problem cannot be addressed directly. The statement of the problem must be analyzed into factors that can be dealt with through intervention by the client and his or her counselor.

Example: Exhibit an ability to experience stress and free time without resorting to drug usage.

3.   **Treatment objectives:** This is a very simple component of a treatment plan taking the stated problems or conditions and converting them into an action statement indicating what needs to be done to reach the goal. For example: Problem statement - Illegal stimulant use. Objective – Keep a log of all thoughts related to stimulant use.

Also, what client factors or behaviors can and need to be changed to alleviate the problem? What is the planned intervention? How does the counselor and the client plan to alter high-risk factors and maladaptive behaviors? Objectives are step-by-step procedures involving behavioral change and then practice to reach the goal. How will the counselor and client know that the problem has been alleviated? Did the treatment strategies work the way they were anticipated?

Assignments or objectives that are given to clients are designed to cause the client to process information surrounding the identified problem which they will then take to group, individual or family sessions. Assignments are not "therapy"; they prepare clients for "therapy".

Example: Client will identify and make a list of ten activities he/she enjoys or would enjoy during free time. Client will become involved in one of these activities every weekend for ten weeks and report back to the group on the experience. At the end of the ten weeks, he/she will identify three activities that provided the most enjoyment.

Note that the objective is directly related to the client's presenting problem. Also notice that measurement is implied in most statements of the objective, i.e., abstinence. Changes in some events are obviously more difficult to measure and require more creativity to assess than others. The measurement of abstinence is no easy task in some situations.

The intervention should logically strengthen a client's weaknesses and reduce the client's problems. In other words, there should be a logical connection between the problems addressed by the treatment plan and the proposed intervention. For example, if use of cocaine is the specified problem, the intervention should propose how to strengthen the client's ability to refrain from using cocaine.

To implement any intervention plan, the counselor has to break the plan into various elements. For example, to establish abstinence from stimulants, the elements may include a period of detoxification followed by a number of days of inpatient treatment (which also has various elements), followed by a period of short-term residential treatment or intensive outpatient treatment and involvement in a self-help group. For each of these activities, a timetable containing a beginning date and completion date should be established. As the counselor and client set out their program of intervention they, in effect, are implementing the treatment plan.

In designing the intervention, it should be remembered that both administrative and programmatic issues must be addressed. In other words, the counselor needs to think not only of a treatment plan but also necessary resources to implement the treatment plan, such as referrals to internal or external resources.

Upon a client's discharge the counselor will be required to provide an end of treatment report, often referred to as a discharge summary. Thus, much of what the counselor will have to report should be related to the treatment plan activities and the "work" accomplished.

Here is a brief example of a treatment plan for a residential program client.

Name: Justin Due

Date of Admission: 6/4/2008   Anticipated Discharge: 7/3/2008

Type of Treatment Program: Residential Program

PROBLEM STATEMENT #4: Justin has a long history of "talking a good talk" about changes he will make but does not follow through by changing behaviors. He exhibits a grandiose sense of self-importance and lacks an objective viewpoint of himself as others see him.

GOAL: Gain an understanding of how he is viewed by others and what they guess is behind the surface image he portrays.

1st OBJECTIVE: Draw a picture of a house that is a representation of himself, signifying what people see on the outside and what they would see differently if they were on the inside. Share this with the group immediately after completing Objective #2.

2nd OBJECTIVE: Ask the group to spend 15 minutes giving input as to negative attributes they have seen in him, followed by 15 minutes of positive attributes they see; do in group on 6/11/2008.

From the Client's Point of View

When a client wants to get well, the treatment plan is most often looked upon with interest and expectation. Client involvement in the treatment planning process is important and a required function for a counselor. Clients, however, will vary in their willingness and skill. Not all clients will be knowledgeable of what might work to address a specific problem. Most will have a general idea that their abuse of substances must stop. However, if they had the "how" answer, they probably would not need a counselor or a treatment program.

When a client is in denial or resents being in a treatment program the treatment plan is likely to be viewed by the client as a hassle. Hence, his or her participation in the treatment planning process will most likely be limited or nonexistent in the initial stages, and the client's affect may vary from being passive to downright angry. His or her behavior may vary from doing nothing, to opposing the treatment plan, or accepting the plan.

From the Counselor's Point of View

Treatment planning should be viewed by a counselor as an important process, much as a contract between the counselor and the client. Just as contracts are typically negotiated, so too should treatment plans. In negotiating with the client, many counseling skills are required, especially motivational interviewing techniques and solution-focused strategies.

It is important for the counselor not to overlook the therapeutic effect of the treatment planning process. The counselor needs to listen, reflect, explain, and problem solve. Failure to do this may result in the client not only misunderstanding what needs to be done but may lead to the client sabotaging the plan. Self-defeating behaviors are not uncommon among substance abusers.

Yet for counselors to listen, reflect, explain, and problem solve while meeting the voluminous administrative requirements for preparing a treatment plan may seem overly demanding. Developing an individualized treatment plan can be overwhelming, especially when counselor stress is high and there is an overload of paper work to complete. Nonetheless, treatment programs should have a treatment plan format for counselors to use. In fact, a well-done treatment plan will make the long-term work of a counselor much easier.

Some, however, in their attempts to decrease paperwork have "boiler-plate" treatment plans for fill in the blank or microcomputer use. Each plan is like all the others. Their clients all sound alike. Objectives are the same for each client in the program. On the other hand, reviewing agencies usually require that each treatment plan be individualized to each client. Therefore, standard treatment plans are not appropriate. Yet with experience and planning, a counselor should be able to develop a repertoire of statements of client goals, objectives, and intervention activities appropriate for customizing a plan for each client. This will make their administrative tasks easier and they will still be able to take into account the strengths and needs of individual clients.

The following figure visually depicts the sequence from problem identification through accomplishment of various objectives or steps toward reaching a client's goal.

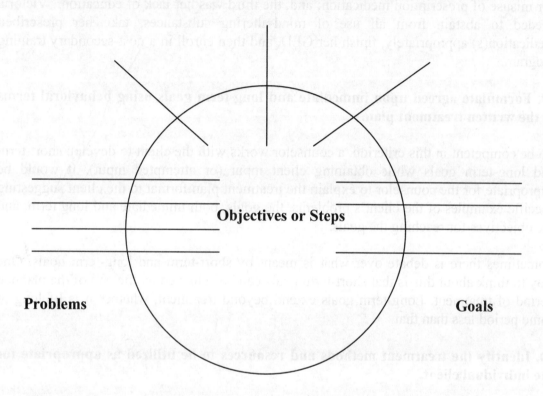

Global Criteria

17. Explain assessment results to the client in an understandable manner.

To be competent in this criterion, a counselor will need to know how to best explain the results of the assessment to the client. In this global criterion, a counselor could begin his or her explanation by paraphrasing the treatment planning core function definition to the client. During the explanation the counselor would need to be clear in describing how the "facts" identified in the assessment are related to the client's presenting problems. In order to facilitate the client's participation in the treatment plan, the competent counselor solicits understanding, feedback and input from the client so that there can be a resolution of the client's presenting problems.

18. Identify and rank problems based on individual client needs in the written treatment plan.

To be competent in this criterion, a counselor specifically identifies, in rank order, the client's presenting problems. The counselor then relates the client's problems to the client's needs. For example, Leslie might relate that in her assessment, Victoria presented three problems. The first problem was her abuse of alcohol; the second was her misuse of prescription medication; and, the third was her lack of education. Victoria needed to abstain from all use of mind-altering substances, take her prescribed medication(s) appropriately, finish her GED, and then enroll in a post-secondary training program.

19. Formulate agreed upon immediate and long-term goals using behavioral terms in the written treatment plan.

To be competent in this criterion, a counselor works with the client to develop short-term and long-term goals while obtaining client input (or attempted input). It would be appropriate for the counselor to explain the treatment plan format to the client suggesting specific examples of the client's problems, the goals, both immediate and long term, and the objectives for reaching the goals.

Sometimes there is debate over what is meant by short-term and long-term goals. One way to think about this is that short-term goals can be achieved by the end of the planned period of treatment. Long-term goals extend beyond treatment, whether it is lifelong or some period less than that.

20. Identify the treatment methods and resources to be utilized as appropriate for the individual client.

To be competent in this criterion, a counselor is knowledgeable about available treatment methods used by the treatment agency, e.g., education classes, individual, group and family counseling sessions. Alcohol and other drug abuse problems do not exist as a result of one condition, thus a multiple method plan is expected. Resources, both within and outside the agency, are listed on the treatment plan.

As I mentioned in Chapter 1, global criteria represent the skills considered important for a counselor to demonstrate competence in the 12 core functions. In the Certified Alcohol and Other Drug Abuse Counselor Job Task Analysis Report 2008 published by the IC&RC both knowledge AND skills were incorporated as tasks into 8 Performance Domains. It is important for the substance abuse counselor to be both knowledgeable AND skillful in his or her capacity as a substance abuse counselor. The core function of Treatment Planning is included in Domain 2, Treatment Planning and the following are the tasks in the Domain of Treatment Planning:

Domain 2: Treatment Planning

- Discuss diagnostic assessment and recommendations with the client and concerned others to initiate an individualized treatment plan that incorporates client's strengths, needs, abilities, and preferences.
- Formulate and prioritize mutually agreed upon problems, immediate and long-term goals, measurable objectives, and treatment methods based upon assessment findings for the purpose of facilitating a course of treatment.

Use ongoing assessment and collaboration with the client to review and modify the treatment plan to address treatment needs.

Assignments

1.   Develop your own script for explaining various assessment results to a client in an understandable manner.

2.   Write three objectives for a presenting problem of your choosing.

3.   Explain how a treatment plan may be different for a client diagnosed as an alcohol abuser as opposed to someone who is diagnosed as alcohol dependent.

4.   Develop a possible treatment plan for a high-school-aged male abuser of methamphetamine with a dual diagnosis of conduct disorder.

5.   Develop a possible treatment plan for a female client who is alcohol dependent and has depression.

6.   Identify the possible resources likely to be found within a residential treatment program.

7.   Identify possible resources likely to be found within an outpatient program.

8.   Identify possible resources likely to be found within a client's home community.

Notes

Chapter 7 - Counseling

IC&RC defines Counseling as **the utilization of special skills to assist individuals, families, or groups in achieving objectives through exploration of a problem and its ramifications; examination of attitudes and feelings; consideration of alternative solutions; and decision making.**

TAP 21 includes the core function of COUNSELING in Domain V and it incorporates three elements: Individual Counseling; Group Counseling; and, Counseling Families, Couples, and Significant Others.

TAP 21 Definition of COUNSELING: A collaborative process that facilitates the client's progress toward mutually determined treatment goals and objectives. Counseling includes methods that are sensitive to individual client characteristics and to the influence of significant others, as well as the client's cultural and social context. Competence in counseling is built on an understanding of, appreciation of, and ability to appropriately use the contributions of various addiction counseling models as they apply to modalities of care for individuals, groups, families, couples, and significant others.

The counseling function is generally viewed by people in the alcohol and drug abuse counseling field as the most important, most critical, and most frequent function of a counselor. Thus, it is imperative for a counselor to be knowledgeable and competent in counseling so as not to do harm to a client, the client's family, or other group.

Within the helping professions there is often a distinction made between counseling and therapy. Therapy is provided by a therapist who is typically a doctoral level clinical psychologist, a master's level social worker, or a psychiatrist. Counseling is provided by a variety of trained professionals and includes pastoral counselors, professional counselors, addiction counselors, school counselors, and others. Because counseling is a therapeutic process, this book does not make a distinction between counseling and therapy and describes the function of counseling of alcohol and drug abuse counselors.

The counseling process establishes a relationship between a counselor and his or her client. Effective counseling facilitates client's problem identification, attitudes and values modification, and behavior changes. The effective counselor bases his or her counseling on an examination of alternative solutions to the presenting problems of a client and the client's active involvement in decision-making.

There are many counseling theories and methods. Some have proven to be more effective than others for specific clients or their specific problems. The research in addiction work does identify "best-practices" and it is incumbent on each counselor to know the research and to personally apply "best-practices" to his or her individual work with clients. It is the competent counselor's responsibility to develop expertise in a number of counseling methods in order to apply the most appropriate methods to a particular client's needs. Many entry-level counselors identify themselves as "eclectic".

The word "eclectic" has two common meanings: One is that the counselor knows a number of theories and their application, but is master of none. A second and one I personally wish for you is that the counselor knows a few theories and their application and knows when to use what theory and techniques with each presenting problem. Within the counseling process, more than one method may be appropriately used.

There are many counseling methods currently employed by counselors. These include, for example, rational emotive therapy, rational behavioral therapy, cognitive therapy, cognitive-behavioral therapy, reality therapy, transactional analysis, gestalt therapy, strategic family therapy, behavior therapy, client-centered therapy, solution-focused therapy, and 12-step facilitated therapy, among others. It is the competent counselor's responsibility to know not only what counseling methods work but also what works best with clients who exhibit certain characteristics.

This author participated on a panel sponsored by the Office of Substance Abuse Treatment (OSAT) and assisted in the development of a Treatment Improvement Protocol (TIP 34) called, *Brief Interventions and Brief Therapies of Substance Abuse*. This TIP provides an excellent review of "brief" methods for providing not only interventions, but also treatment for substance abusers. It is an excellent resource for theories and techniques of counseling with substance abusers.

When counselors try to explain what they do in counseling, an infrequent but common error is made. Some counselors attempt to demonstrate their skills in the core function of counseling by referencing the 12-step work of Alcoholics Anonymous (AA). AA is a support group that many believe is important (or essential) for recovery from substance addiction. AA is appropriate to reference in the core functions of treatment planning, client education, referral, and perhaps crisis intervention, but not necessarily in counseling. Knowing appropriate theories, a competent counselor can apply 12-step principles in a counseling relationship. "Best practices" refers to this as 12-step facilitated therapy. For example, The Serenity Prayer is an excellent cognitive-behavioral statement that advances cognitive understanding, incorporates motivational self-talk, and behavioral change. It is essential for the beginning counselor to be able to demonstrate knowledge and skills when implementing specific counseling methods and techniques with individuals, families, and groups.

A counselor also should be aware of the limitations and issues imposed by the current state of the science and art of professional counseling. For example, in the last few years, with an increased concern about cultural, gender, and life-style differences among clients and counselors, a number of questions are being asked.

How would you answer the following questions?

1. When counseling persons from other subcultures, can counselors be effective if they have not had multicultural counseling training?

2. If multicultural training is a prerequisite to multicultural counseling competence, what kind and how much training is necessary?

3. What specifically makes for effective multicultural counseling?

4. Is it important to acknowledge and demonstrate appreciation for a client's culture?

5. Is it important to understand a client's socio-cultural background, influences, and stressors?

6. Does a counselor need to understand the family dynamics and social roles of each client served?

From the Client's Point of View

After admission to a treatment program, a client expects counseling. Even if the client is ordered by a court to appear for counseling or is in denial, there is an expectation that counseling will occur whether wanted or not. The client usually does not know what counseling method, theory, or approach is being used, just that "it is happening."

Clients entering treatment often believe their lives are out of control, what is known as unmanageability. They may feel scared, alone, confused, angry, depressed, anxious, and many other feelings. They may at the same time have some hope that counseling will help them or you, the counselor, will fix them. A client may not trust him or herself or others to be able to solve his or her problems, yet may want help. Some will want help but not the hard "work" required. They hold a belief that "Life should be easy". There is often the fear of failure, so some ask "why try?" Clients in denial or in involuntary treatment often become angry, even hostile. This is to be expected since their thoughts may be, "I don't have a problem!" or "I shouldn't be here!"

In time, as the counseling process takes place, such negative feelings may change. As a client's negative behaviors decrease, there is a corresponding increase in feelings of positive self-worth, contentment and increased hope. Even the involuntary client's negative feelings frequently mellow. This is true even if they do not accept the idea that they have a problem. These clients may credit the counselor, their treatment program, or even a significant other for these changes in feelings. Initially most clients will not take credit for any changes in their feelings. Only with continued counseling and support do most clients come to understand they are responsible for their behavior and feelings. As they gain in this understanding they take credit for changes in their maladaptive behavior and negative feelings.

From the Counselor's Point of View

Counseling is the "heart and soul" for many counselors. It is their personal choice, their career. It is what they do for a living. They did not just become counselors; they made serious choices in order to be counselors. Many come from a background of their own addiction. Many authors have discussed the "why" of working in a helping profession like counseling. Their reasons range from idealism, wanting to help others, to being in recovery and deciding to give something back.

In beginning a training program to become a counselor, counselor trainees are often somewhat overwhelmed with all the theories and techniques of counseling that they are expected to learn. Some approaches such as psychoanalysis, take years of professional study. Yet all approaches take time to learn. All approaches require a strong foundation in personality theory and human development. The IC&RC standards required for certification as an alcohol and drug abuse counselor specify the particular aspects of this required foundation. It is a foundation that is knowledge, skill, and experience based. A college degree, even a doctorate, is not enough.

To be an alcohol and drug abuse counselor one needs to complete the following:

- 270 hours of education in the knowledge and skills of alcohol and drug use and abuse;

- three years of supervised experience;

- 300 hours of direct supervision, at least 10 hours in each of the 12 core functions;

- demonstration of competence and skill in substance abuse knowledge by passing a written test;

- adherence to a strict code of ethics.

In other words, counseling is a well-developed professional field Counselors may not carry the educational history and prestige of a physician but today, the certified counselor can be proud of the development and social recognition of the substance abuse counseling field. Substance abuse counselors have labored in the war on drugs, demonstrated their value by the many they have helped to be in the stage of recovery, and gained the respect of many. This is reflected in such actions as more and more insurance companies are recognizing and accepting the credentials of substance abuse counselors. Additionally, there are "advanced" credentials offered in many states and countries to recognize further development of counseling skills and specialization.

Global Criteria

21. Select the counseling theory (ies) that apply (ies).

To be minimally competent in this criterion, a counselor would need to know at least one counseling theory that is applicable to a client and the client's presenting problem(s). Here is where a course on counseling theories and techniques begins to build counselor competence. "Best practices" research identifies cognitive-behavioral theory as perhaps the theory with the most promising efficacy in the field of substance abuse treatment. That does not mean that other theories are not.

Although one counseling approach or method may be used predominately during counseling, a counselor should be able to utilize the most appropriate approach for a client's presenting problem or need. As I mentioned earlier in this chapter, it is important for a counselor to be proficient in one or two counseling theories and corresponding techniques and to know when to best use those techniques within the framework of a theory. For example, a counselor might know that initially in the counseling process a client-centered approach, perhaps using motivational interviewing techniques, is appropriate in order to convey empathy and unconditional positive regard for the client. Later, as rapport is established, a counselor might implement the treatment plan using a reality-therapy approach in order to confront the client with "the facts" of the client's presenting problem; or, the counselor may then use a cognitive-behavioral therapy approach during individual or group counseling to help the client become aware of feelings and maladaptive behaviors that are the result of the client's self-defeating thinking processes. The counselor might involve the client's family in the treatment by using a strategic-family therapy approach.

Although selecting a counseling theory or theories is all that the IC&RC initially expects in this global criterion, a competent counselor would know the rationale for selecting the chosen theory(ies). A competent counselor should be able to describe the selection and explain the rationale sequentially from the beginning of the counseling process to discharge.

22. Apply technique(s) to assist the client, group, and/or family in exploring problems and ramifications.

To be competent in this criterion, a counselor would be able to describe multiple examples of counseling techniques, hopefully related to his or her chosen counseling theory. The counselor should know "how" the client's presenting problems are explored and "what" the ramifications of the presenting problems are. Knowing "buzz words" and the mere mention of a well-known technique does not suggest competence. For example, a counselor should not be limited to, "I used journaling to have the client identify the ramifications of his problem with alcohol." Instead, the counselor using journaling would know what journaling is, how the client would come to understand the technique, and what the client and counselor does with journal writing during the counseling process.

The following techniques comprise a partial list frequently used in a counselor's exploration of a client's problems and ramifications. Keep in mind that each technique needs to be understood in light of this criterion.

Timeline	Confrontation	Loss List
Interferences	Autobiography	Signs and Symptoms List
V-Chart	Financial Losses	Life Script
Life Style	The Wall	Body Maps
Johari Window	Family Sculpture	Letters In
Sack Collage	ABCs	Symptoms Assignment
Open-Ended Questions	Empathic Responding	Irrational Belief List
Relationship Maps	Loss List	Anger Log
Stimulus-Response	Time Line	Journaling

The following graphic helps to clarify the difference between this criterion and the next criterion.

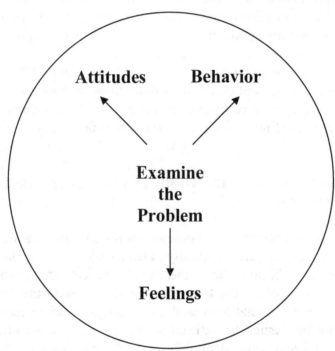

After a counselor uses techniques to examine the problem, then a transition can take place towards examining a client's behavior, attitudes, and feelings using additional appropriate techniques.

23. Apply technique(s) to assist the client, group, and/or family in examining the client's behavior, attitudes, and/or feelings if appropriate in the treatment setting.

To be competence in this criterion, a counselor would need to again know multiple examples of techniques. The counseling techniques need to be identified and described. A counselor should know how to explain "how" a client's behavior, attitudes, and feelings are examined and "what" results are expected. A counselor should again avoid the use of "buzz words" and the mere mention of even a well-known technique. For example, if an empty-chair technique is used with a client, a counselor should be able to explain the rationale for the technique, how the technique was used with the client, and what the expected results of using the technique are.

Again, although not exhaustive, the following list of techniques frequently addresses the examination of a client' behavior, attitudes, and feelings:

Empty Chair	Letter Writing (out)	Good Will Box
Collage	Role Playing	Psycho Drama
Journaling	Peer Evaluation	Two Chair
Responsible Position	Art	Their Shoes
Cognitive Restructuring	Shame Attacking	Disputing Beliefs
Rational Self-Analysis	Imagery	Behavior Contract
Scaling Questions	Problem Solving	Alternatives

24. Individualize counseling in accordance with cultural, gender, and lifestyle differences.

To be competent in this criterion, a counselor knows how counseling is individualized to take into account the client's culture, gender, and lifestyle. Counselors who share the same culture, gender, or lifestyle as their clients may have an easier time in individualizing treatment plans than other counselors. Nonetheless, counselors should not assume that this criterion does not apply. All counseling should be individualized to take into account the particular characteristics of clients — and any counselor should be able to demonstrate skill at individualizing the counseling process for each client.

For competence in this criterion, a counselor understands a client's subculture, takes into account the client's gender, and understands the client's lifestyle. A counselor would be aware of any of these characteristics if unusual for the client's treatment setting or the counselor's professional experience. It is a counselor's responsibility to be aware of areas such as cultural diversity and to know what issues and techniques are appropriate for various subcultures and ethnic populations.

It is the counselor's responsibility to individualize the counseling for the client's gender. For example, a female counselor may have been assigned to a female client because of the client's past history of being sexually assaulted.

Individualizing the counseling based upon a client's lifestyle is also the counselor's responsibility. Lifestyle generally refers to the living experience of the client and, for example, may mean bachelorhood, married life, a homosexual relationship, being a housewife, or a professional with a hectic schedule (such as a physician).

A counselor's responsibility is to be competent in knowing how counseling can be individualized for the client. Do not confuse "individualize counseling" with individualizing the client's treatment plan alone.   A counselor understands how the counseling is individualized not other services.

25. Interact with the client in an appropriate therapeutic manner.

Ethics, boundaries and more ethics! To be competent in this criterion, a counselor needs to know ethical standards of behavior and practice appropriate boundaries in all contact with clients. This starts with screening and continues well beyond the treatment episode.

This criterion can be evaluated on a knowledge test, such as the IC&RC written examination, with questions about ethics and boundaries. More importantly, a counselor's actions should be observed by the counselor's supervisor and even peers with ethics and boundary violations reported to the certification or licensing board. There should never be evidence of ethical or boundary violations. If ever in doubt, seek consultation.

26. Elicit alternative solutions and decisions from the client.

To be competent in this criterion, a counselor would again need to know multiple techniques to elicit alternative solutions for the client's presenting problem from the client. A counselor engages the client in problem-solving and decision-making processes. This criterion is an excellent one for a counselor to use solution-focused or brief therapy techniques to help a client find alternative solutions and for the client to make decisions. For example, the counselor might ask a client to brainstorm possible solutions to a problem —such as his or her feelings or obligation to stop at the pub with friends — and that once possible solutions are identified, the client makes a list of pros and cons for each of the possible solutions. Another example would be a counselor using a client-centered approach helps a client discover a solution to a specific problem such as low self-worth related to a lack of vocational training, and then facilitates the client to act on that discovery.

Criteria 22, 23, and 26 all specifically relate to counseling skills and techniques. These three criteria are the "heart" of what most counselors consider counseling.

27. Implement the treatment plan.

To be competent in this criterion, a counselor would need to understand that the counseling core function directly relates to the treatment plan developed for each client. There should be a logical connection between treatment goals, objectives, and activities detailed in the treatment plan and what is done during counseling, both group and in individual. The counselor makes the connection between counseling as an activity and the objectives in the plan.

This criterion is very difficult to evaluate on a written examination; however, during supervision sessions and during observations of a counselor's counseling, this criterion can aptly be evaluated.

As I mentioned in Chapter 1, global criteria represent the skills considered important for a counselor to demonstrate competence in the 12 core functions. In the Certified Alcohol and Other Drug Abuse Counselor Job Task Analysis Report 2008 published by the IC&RC both knowledge AND skills are incorporated as tasks into 8 Performance Domains. It is important for the substance abuse counselor to be both knowledgeable AND skillful in his or her capacity as a substance abuse counselor. The core function of Counseling is included in Domain 5, Counseling and the following are the tasks in the Domain of Counseling:

Domain 5: Counseling

- Develop a therapeutic relationship with clients, families, and concerned others in order to facilitate self-exploration, disclosure, and problem solving.
- Educate the client regarding the structure, expectations, and limitations of the counseling process.
- Utilize individual and group counseling strategies and modalities to match the interventions with the client's level of readiness.
- Continually evaluate the client's level of risk regarding personal safety and relapse potential in order to anticipate and respond to crisis situations.
- Apply selected counseling strategies in order to enhance treatment effectiveness and facilitate progress towards completion of treatment objectives.
- Adapt counseling strategies to match the client's needs including abilities, gender, sexual orientation, developmental level, culture, ethnicity, age, and health status.
- Evaluate the effectiveness of counseling strategies based on the client's progress in order to determine the need to modify treatment strategies and treatment objectives.
- Develop an effective continuum of recovery plan with the client in order to strengthen ongoing recovery outside of primary treatment.
- Assist families and concerned others in understanding substance use disorders and utilizing strategies that sustain recovery and maintain healthy relationships.
- Document counseling activity to record all relevant aspects of treatment.

Assignments

1. Write a one-page description of the following counseling approaches:

   a. Cognitive Therapy
   b. Rational Emotive Therapy
   c. Rational Behavioral Therapy
   d. Reality Therapy
   e. Transactional Analysis
   f. Gestalt Therapy
   g. Strategic Family Therapy
   h. Behavior Therapy
   i. Client-Centered Therapy

2.   Write a one-page rationale for the counseling approaches listed in assignment #1 above for an alcohol or other drug abusing client.

3.   For each of the counseling approaches listed in assignment #1 above, describe at least two techniques that could be appropriately used to explore a client's presenting problems and their ramifications.

4.   For each of the techniques listed in Criterion 22, research and write a description of the technique to share with other class members. Be sure to identify how the technique is used to explore a client's presenting problems and their ramifications.

5.   For each of the counseling approaches listed in assignment #1 above, describe at least two techniques that could be used to assist a client, group, or family in examining a client's behavior, attitudes, and feelings.

6.   For each of the techniques listed in Criterion 23, research and write a description of the technique to share with other class members. Be sure to identify how the technique is used to assist a client, group, or family in examining a client's behavior, attitudes, and feelings.

7.   How might a counseling approach be individualized for a single gay mother?

8.   How might a counseling approach be individualized for a client when English is the second language?

9.   Identify and then discuss two inappropriate interactions with a client.

10. For each of the counseling approaches listed in assignment #1 above, describe at least two techniques that could be used to elicit solutions and decisions from a client.

11. Identify and then discuss a counseling issue that would result in a change to the treatment plan of a client.

12. Identify and then discuss the three possible ethical violations that could occur during the counseling function.

13. How long after discharge can a counselor date a client? Provide the rationale for your answer.

Notes

Notes

Chapter 8 - Case Management

IC&RC defines CASE MANAGEMENT as **activities intended to bring services, agencies, resources, or people together within a planned framework of action toward the achievement of established goals. It may involve liaison activities and collateral contacts.**

TAP 21 includes the core function of CASE MANAGEMENT in Domain IV, Service Coordination and it incorporates three elements: Implementing the Treatment Plan; Consulting; and, Continuing Assessment and Treatment Planning

TAP 21 Definition of SERVICE COORDINATION: The administrative, clinical, and evaluative activities that bring the client, treatment services, community agencies, and other resources together to focus on issues and needs identified in the treatment plan. Service coordination, which includes case management and client advocacy, establishes a framework of action to enable the client to achieve specified goals. It involves collaboration with the client and significant others, coordination of treatment and referral services, liaison activities with community resources and managed care systems, client advocacy, and ongoing evaluation of treatment progress and client needs.

The function of case management is administrative support of the client's therapeutic goals. Case management is the coordination of activities and services for a client in order to facilitate the positive outcome of the treatment plan. Coordination implies the involvement of more than one person in making sure that plans are carried out successfully.

In managing the case of a client, a counselor may use consultation and referral functions. However, case management is more than either of those functions individually. To describe consultation or referral as case management is mistaken. Case management is the comprehensive coordination of all aspects of the client's treatment plan. It does not exist in a vacuum nor is it time-limited within the overall treatment process. Case management activity begins with the initial treatment plan and continues throughout treatment to discharge and aftercare.

In some larger agencies the function of case management is assigned to a case manager. This person does not need to be a counselor in order to conduct the function of case management. While a person with good administrative or management skills can competently coordinate services, in most agencies each client's individual counselor provides the case management.

Throughout the treatment process, a counselor is required to explain to the client what is happening, to orient the client to the program, explain the treatment plan, explain the rationale for various consultations and referrals, explain the need to obtain written permission for the release of confidential information, and to explain the rationale for case management.

From the Client's Point of View

To a client, case management is one of those functions taken for granted. Most clients are aware that their case is being managed but they do not need to fully understand the process. It would be much like knowing that a computer has a disk operating system but not needing to know how to do the actual programming nor fully understand the system — only that "it works."

From the Counselor's Point of View

A counselor needs to realize that he or she is responsible for the client's care. The idealized goal for all treatment is to have the client *not* experience any ongoing problems with substance use. How this is accomplished is the essence of case management. It is the coordination of all the activities brought together to reach this idealized goal.

In other words, success in treatment relies heavily on case management and getting the right services to the client at the right time. Case management is time sensitive. Thus, a counselor must know when during the treatment process specific activities are most likely to be successful.

Global Criteria

28. Explain the rationale of case management activities to the client.

To be competent in this criterion, a counselor understands that the explanation for case management services is given to the client, briefly stating the rationale, and answering any client questions.

As an example of one case management activity, Victoria could say to Leslie "Leslie. We've identified your need to furthering your education as a goal. At this time I'd like to coordinate a meeting with you and a representative from the community college so that you can understand what is required and to begin that process".

29. Coordinate services for client care.

To be competent in this criterion, a counselor knows how to explain and describe how client services are coordinated and then actually doing the coordination. Competence is displayed by understanding and implementing the traditional who, what, when, where, and why questions. Who does the counselor coordinate with? What needs coordinated? When, during the treatment process, is the coordination completed? Where is the coordination completed? Why is there a need for the coordination of services? A counselor should be able to answer each of these questions for each client on his or her case load.

As I mentioned in Chapter 1, global criteria represent the skills considered important for a counselor to demonstrate competence in the 12 core functions. In the Certified Alcohol and Other Drug Abuse Counselor Job Task Analysis Report 2008 published by the

IC&RC both knowledge AND skills were incorporated as tasks into 8 Performance Domains. It is important for the substance abuse counselor to be both knowledgeable AND skillful in his or her capacity as a substance abuse counselor. The core function of Case Management is included in Domain 4, Service Coordination and the following is the tasks in the Domain of Service Coordination:

Domain 4: Service Coordination

- Identify and maintain information about current community resources in order to meet identified client needs.
- Communicate with community resources concerning relevant client information to meet the identified needs of the client.
- Advocate for the client in areas of identified needs to facilitate continuity of care.
- Evaluate the effectiveness of case management activities through collaboration with the client, treatment team members, and community resources to ensure quality service coordination.
- Consult with the client, family, and concerned others to make appropriate changes to the treatment plan ensuring progress toward treatment goals.
- Prepare accurate and concise screening, intake, and assessment documents.

Assignments

1. Develop a "fictional" flow chart for the coordination of services for a client.

2. Develop your own script for explaining case management services to a client in an understandable manner.

3. What factors and issues would you consider in the case management of an HIV-positive client?

4. Interview a nutritionist and prepare a description of the relationship of nutrition to a substance abuser's health.

5. What issues might a counselor encounter in dealing with a probation officer while case managing a client's care?

6. How is case management different in a solo outpatient private practice as opposed to a large inpatient program?

Notes

The client cannot use drugs at all because she is HIV/AIDS it will just make it worse. Besides she has children to take care of on her own but she also needs to be careful and get educated on the other drug of choice, cannot be using it at all. She needs attend meetings three times a day. If the meetings she attends are not working for her then she will need to be admitted to a facility and her children will have to go to her mother until she gets better.

Chapter 9 - Crisis Intervention

IC&RC defines CRISIS INTERVENTION as **those services which respond to an alcohol and/or other drug abuser's needs during acute emotional and/or physical distress.**

TAP 21 includes the core function of CRISIS INTERVENTION in Domain I – CLINICAL EVALUATION.

TAP 21 Definition of Clinical Evaluation: The systematic approach to screening and assessment of individuals thought to have a substance use disorder, being considered for admission to addiction-related services, or presenting in a crisis situation.

Thus, TAP 21's definition of Clinical Evaluation includes three (3) core functions: Screening; Assessment; and, Crisis Intervention. TAP 21 does not specifically define an element for Crisis Intervention.

The key words in this definition are services, abuser's needs, and acute distress. The most important word is acute. All clients, by nature of their being clients, are in some state of crisis. The core function of crisis intervention, however, relates to a counselor's services to their client when there has likely been some precipitating event to shift the client from the usual state of conflict or crisis to an intense state of acute distress. With little exception, the client, not the counselor or some textbook, determines a crisis. One client's crisis may be a usual state of affairs for another. The exception is when a client is actively a threat to harm self or others. Other events such as death, serious injury, or new diagnosis of a serious condition may result in a crisis for many clients, but not all.

In order to determine that a client is in a crisis state, a counselor first must be aware of a conflict between the client and the client's total situation. The conflict must have new potential for overwhelming the client, perhaps to self-harm, and a low likelihood of the client being able to resolve this new conflict or situation by him or herself. In this condition, a crisis state exists and the competent counselor should intervene.

Many books have been written about crisis intervention. As a core function of the substance abuse counselor, crisis intervention is an important and critical function. Skill in this function is frequently required in a "hot-line" situation and crises perhaps are less common in the day-to-day experience of most counselors. However, each counselor seeking certification must have skill in all three criteria of this core function.

For competence, a counselor must be able to recognize the elements of a crisis state, know the steps necessary to resolve acute distress, and have competence in using the crisis events to enhance the overall treatment services for the client.

Specific skills recognized as necessary for a counselor to be able to intervene in life crisis situations include:

- being able to discern the potential for crises to develop,

- having the skill and knowledge to determine the level of crisis and match the response to the resources available to the counselor,

- knowing and being skilled in crisis intervention techniques,

- knowing emergency first aid, and

- being able to use communication techniques to reframe and deescalate a crisis.

If possible it is important for the counselor to do a "reality check" of the client's situation. Whatever life event the client says happened, be sure to determine first if it really happened. I recall a private client of mine who believed his wife of 30 years was having an affair. Since she was a home-nurse, this could have been within the realm of reality, if not with her disabled patients, then perhaps with some lover. This client, a previously undiagnosed paranoid schizophrenic, related that he had encountered their minister at the store one day. The minister commented, "I saw your wife today." Later that evening, my client asked his wife what the minister had to say to her today. She said she didn't see the minister, which lead him to accuse her of lying about that and of lying about not having an affair. He believed he now had more evidence to prove his wife was a liar and unfaithful to him. With my encouragement, he went to his minister to verify seeing his wife. His minister, somewhat surprised, told my client he had indeed seen his wife going into the drug store from his car but she didn't see him nor did they converse. My client was in crisis over the precipitating event of finding his wife lying; however, his thinking was not based upon fact. As an alcohol and drug abuse counselor, it is important to verify, when possible, the nature and circumstances of the precipitating event for the client. In reality, this is not always possible.

In my graduate counseling class at Doane College, I do a segment on crisis intervention. I used the global criteria of Crisis Intervention to aid these counselors in training. I recall one student's excellent write-up of dealing with a crisis regarding a client. The only problem was that no crisis occurred. The counselor had done an outstanding job of recognizing the potential for a crisis and took active steps to avoid a crisis so that no crisis then existed. It is imperative that the beginning counselor understands that a crisis is client determined, not the counselor.

From the Client's Point of View

A client in crisis is likely to be in considerable distress. The client sees some precipitating life event as awful and terrible — "this shouldn't be happening to me;" "I can't stand this." Often the precipitating event leads the client into a vicious cycle of self-defeating thoughts and feelings, an example of when emotions control the client. These, in turn, lead to behavior that may be harmful to the client or to another person.

From the Counselor's Point of View

Dealing with a client in crisis is often a stressful task for the counselor. Not doing well or not doing the "right thing" may even result in the death of the client. There is no other counselor function that has such possible consequences. *Semper paratus*— always prepared — seems to be an appropriate motto.

Global Criteria

30. Recognize the elements of the client crisis.

To be competent in this criterion, a counselor should know the elements of a crisis and be able to relate the elements to an actual client. A counselor needs to understand the predisposing factors present before the precipitating event, describe the crisis event, and describe the client's responses to include feelings and behaviors of the client. A counselor needs to answer questions such as, "What is the crisis?" and "Why is this a crisis for this client?"

31. Implement an immediate course of action appropriate to the crisis.

To be competent in this criterion, a counselor knows the steps that should be followed for a specific client's crisis. It is important that the counselor know immediate actions that are appropriate to the nature of the crisis. There is usually a series of steps for a counselor to take in a number of crisis situations, for example, calling 911, checking for safety, determining whether a plan exists for doing harm to self or others, and determining supports that the client has available. Insuring a client's safety and the safety of others is a continuous responsibility of the counselor until the client is no longer under the counselor's care.

32. Enhance overall treatment by utilizing crisis events.

To be competent in this criterion, a counselor relates the crisis to the current treatment plan or its revision, and understands how a crisis can be used within the counseling, referral or consultation core functions to enhance the client's overall treatment.

Sequentially, this criterion addresses what a counselor does after the crisis is resolved. A crisis event can often be used to enhance treatment; to gain insight into other effective methods of treatment; and may result in a revision of the client's treatment plan.

As I mentioned in Chapter 1, global criteria represent the skills considered important for a counselor to demonstrate competence in the 12 core functions. In the Certified Alcohol and Other Drug Abuse Counselor Job Task Analysis Report 2008 published by the IC&RC both knowledge AND skills were incorporated as tasks into 8 Performance Domains. It is important for the substance abuse counselor to be both knowledgeable AND skillful in his or her capacity as a substance abuse counselor. The core function of Crisis Intervention is not a separate domain but is included in Domain 1, Clinical

Evaluation and Domain 5, Counseling and the following are the tasks in those domains that appear to apply to Crisis Intervention:

Domain 1: Clinical Evaluation

- Demonstrate effective verbal and non-verbal communication to establish rapport.
- Assess client's current situation, including signs and symptoms of intoxication and withdrawal, by evaluating observed behavior and other available information to determine client's immediate needs.

Domain 5: Counseling

- Develop a therapeutic relationship with clients, families, and concerned others in order to facilitate self-exploration, disclosure, and problem solving.
- Utilize individual and group counseling strategies and modalities to match the interventions with the client's level of readiness.
- Continually evaluate the client's level of risk regarding personal safety and relapse potential in order to anticipate and respond to crisis situations.
- Apply selected counseling strategies in order to enhance treatment effectiveness and facilitate progress towards completion of treatment objectives.
- Adapt counseling strategies to match the client's needs including abilities, gender, sexual orientation, developmental level, culture, ethnicity, age, and health status.
- Evaluate the effectiveness of counseling strategies based on the client's progress in order to determine the need to modify treatment strategies and treatment objectives.
- Develop an effective continuum of recovery plan with the client in order to strengthen ongoing recovery outside of primary treatment.
- Document counseling activity to record all relevant aspects of treatment.

Assignments

1. Read a book on crisis intervention and prepare a standard book report.

2. Develop a flow chart to visually show the elements of a crisis.

3. Identify two possible crises of a client and describe an appropriate course of action you might take to resolve the crisis.

4. Identify two possible crises of a client and describe how you might use the crisis to enhance the overall treatment of the client.

5. Discuss the legal issues related to the necessity for breaking client confidentiality.

6. Discuss under what conditions a break of confidentiality is acceptable when dealing with a client in crisis.

Notes

Chapter 10 - Client Education

IC&RC defines CLIENT EDUCATION as **provision of information to individuals and groups concerning alcohol and other drug abuse and the available services and resources.**

TAP 21 includes the core function of CLIENT EDUCATION in Domain VI – CLIENT, FAMILY, AND COMMUNITY EDUCATION.

TAP 21 Definition of CLIENT EDUCATION: The process of providing clients, families, significant others, and community groups with information on risks related to psychoactive substance use, as well as available prevention, treatment, and recovery resources.

Client education is an important and frequent activity in the treatment plan of substance abusers. A counselor provides relevant education to a client through formal and informal methods in order to introduce knowledge in support of the treatment process. Additionally, a counselor may provide relevant education to the client's significant others, including family members, to help them acquire the needed knowledge and understanding to also support the recovery process. This includes informing them and members of the client's support group about resources that are available in the community.

Community resources usually include various alcohol and drug abuse support groups like AA, AlAnon, AlAteen, Narcotics Anonymous and Smart Recovery. Additional resources might be other treatment providers such as half-way houses, outpatient substance abuse services and private practitioners.

The education that a counselor provides needs not be limited to information about alcohol or other drugs. Education about substances may be incorporated into presentations or other topics, such as the role of substances in social skills or assertiveness.

Although client education is usually viewed as direct service to an admitted client in a treatment program, the *Role Delineation Study for Alcohol and Other Drug Abuse Counselors* (ICRC/AODA 1996) expanded the scope of client education. In addition to providing substance abuse information to clients, significant others, and family members, the role of the counselor also includes providing alcohol and drug education to schools, service clubs, businesses, industry and labor representatives, political and community leaders, and others to raise awareness and enhance community support for the recovery of people with substance abuse problems. The role of client education also has been expanded to conducting in-service training for peers and colleagues in order to enhance professionalism and assist in the continuum of client care.

A frequent misunderstanding about client education is that some counselors believe that this core function requires them to teach about topics other than substance use and abuse, such as assertiveness or vocational training. Although instruction in a variety of areas is often an appropriate component of the treatment plan, for the alcohol and drug abuse counselor, client education as a core function is limited to education about alcohol and other drugs. In doing so, it is generally accepted that clients need to learn about the disease concept of alcoholism and how their substance use has affected their lives. Thus, client education in alcohol and other drugs is an appropriate activity. To facilitate this education counselors explain the rationale for client education and use appropriate motivational counseling techniques to facilitate the client's understanding and cooperation.

From the Client's Point of View

Given that a treatment plan has been explained to a client, he or she expects to learn about alcohol or other drugs as a part of what will be taught during treatment. In a residential treatment setting, however, clients sometimes associate the education process with being back in school. This may be good or bad depending on the past school experiences of the client.

Some clients get "turned on" with learning about substance abuse. Some will even become compulsive about learning more. Others, especially those with limited education, may get "turned off" and complain about reading, viewing videos, or doing anything academic. This core function allows a counselor to individualize the treatment plan for culture, gender, and lifestyle differences while providing substance use and abuse education.

From the Counselor's Point of View

Trainers of substance abuse counselors often fail to provide the skills needed to function most effectively as an educator as well as a counselor. College courses in substance abuse counseling do not require a "student teaching" practicum, nor do the informal workshops taken by alcohol and drug abuse counselors. Only substance abuse counselors in the military services, and possibly a few others, receive instruction and training to be instructors. Counselors who were certified school teachers also have this background. Most counselors, however, are left to their own resources and receive on-the-job training for conducting classes on substance abuse. Thus, they often overly rely on commercially available films to teach, especially with groups. There seems to be among many the sense that "Who can present the information better than Father Martin in *Chalk Talk?*"

In the more formal setting of a classroom or auditorium, counselors need to employ professional teaching skills. In a more informal setting, counseling skills can be used to enhance learning. This means that the more formal the client education the more likely there should be lesson plans with stated goals and objectives. It makes sense to have an idea of what one wants to teach and how one should go about achieving the desired learning.

In one-on-one situations, there may be less need for lesson plans, lectures, pamphlets, video or audio tapes. Discussion is usually appropriate in a one-on-one settings for teaching clients. A lack of lesson plans, however, should not mean that one is not prepared or one has no agenda as to what needs to be accomplished. This is where the treatment plan has value. The use of materials, such as brochures, pamphlets, and videos can be used to supplement both formal presentations and one-on-one discussions.

Relapse prevention education presents a different kind of challenge to substance abuse counselors than does recovery or community education. Relapse is a progressive pattern of maladaptive behavior by a client that results in the reoccurrence of a problem. A client in relapse is likely to have had a previous experience with client education. As a result a client may feel as if he or she "knows it all" and becomes resistant to further instruction about substance abuse and recovery. In explaining a treatment plan to a client in such a case, the counselor will need to relate why more instruction is related to relapse prevention. In this way the client may gain insight into their relapse and become more focused on completion of another treatment in following the counselor's recommendations.

Global Criteria

33. Present relevant alcohol and other drug use/abuse information to the client through formal and/or informal processes.

To be competent in this criterion, a counselor knows a number of relevant methods for educating the client and applies them as part of a treatment plan to educate a client about substance use and abuse. A counselor may be skilled in formal education methods such as films, handouts on substance abuse issues and lectures, or informal methods such as discussions in the counseling session or the use of bibliotherapy.

34. Present information about available alcohol and other drug services and resources.

To be competent in this criterion, a counselor knows a number of relevant methods, applied as part of the treatment plan, to educate the client about available alcohol and other drug services and resources. The services and resources may be part of the client's current treatment program, i.e., in-house or in the client's home community. A counselor provides examples of these services to the client, family or others and identifies resources. A counselor provides a rationale for the use of a specific service or resource to a client's presenting problem. A counselor needs to have a comprehensive understanding of the available community services and resources.

As I mentioned in Chapter 1, global criteria represent the skills considered important for a counselor to demonstrate competence in the 12 core functions. In the Certified Alcohol and Other Drug Abuse Counselor Job Task Analysis Report 2008 published by the IC&RC both knowledge AND skills were incorporated as tasks into 8 Performance Domains. It is important for the substance abuse counselor to be both knowledgeable AND skillful in his or her capacity as a substance abuse counselor. The core function of Client Education is included in Domain 6, Client, Family and Community Education and the following are the tasks in the Domain of Client, Family and Community Education:

Domain 6: Client, Family and Community Education

- Provide culturally relevant formal and informal education that raises awareness of substance use, prevention, and recovery.
- Provide education on issues of cultural identity, ethnic background, age, sexual orientation, and gender in prevention, treatment, and recovery.
- Provide education on health and high-risk behaviors associated with substance use, including transmission and prevention of HIV/AIDS, tuberculosis, sexually transmitted infections, hepatitis, and other infectious diseases.
- Provide education on life skills, including but not limited to, stress management, relaxation, communication, assertiveness, and refusal skills.
- Provide education on the biological, medical, and physical aspects of substance use to develop an understanding of the effects of chemical substances on the body.
- Provide education on the emotional, cognitive, and behavioral aspects of substance use to develop an understanding of the psychological aspects of substance use, abuse, and addiction.
- Provide education on the sociological and environmental effect of substance use to develop an understanding of the impact of substance use on the affected family systems.
- Provide education on the continuum of care and resources available to develop an understanding of prevention, intervention, treatment, and recovery.

Assignments

1. Develop a list of relevant substance abuse films, videos, books, and other teaching resources to use with clients.

2. Obtain or develop at least 10 handouts appropriate for a client's use in acquiring alcohol or other drug abuse information.

3. Develop a list of local community resources appropriate for clients in aftercare.

4. Compare and contrast AA with Rational Recovery.

5. When would it not be appropriate to refer a client to a self-help group?

6. Research the literature on substance abuse prevention and discuss the implication that information increases knowledge but does not alone change attitudes or behavior. Relate this to providing client education in a treatment setting.

7. Prepare a lesson plan on a specific alcohol or drug topic and share the lesson plan with other staff members or fellow students.

Notes

Notes

Chapter 11 - Referral

IC&RC defines REFERRAL as **the identification of client's needs that cannot be met by the counselor or agency and assisting the client to use the support systems and community resources available**

TAP 21 includes the core function of REFERRAL in Domain III – REFERRAL.

TAP 21 Definition of REFERRAL: The process of facilitating the client's use of available support systems and community resources to meet needs identified in clinical evaluation or treatment planning.

Referral implies that specific information about a client will be released to an outside person or agency. Hence, a client-signed authorization to release information is required before any release of the client's data can occur. By law, the following information is required:

- The client's name,

- birth date,

- the releasing agency's name and address,

- the receiving agency's name and address,

- the specific information to be released,

- the purpose for the release of information,

- an expiration date,

- the event or condition for the release expiration,

- the client's signature, and

- the date signed.

The core function of referral should not be confused with the core function of consultation, a frequent mistake of entry-level counselors. Referral, as explained above, involves the release of client data to someone outside the counselor's agency. Consultation often occurs without the release of client data. In referral, a counselor may say, "I can't do it, but somebody else can." In consultation, a counselor may say, "I can do it, but I can do it better with another's help."

In the referral core function, the counselor recognizes one's own limits and the needs of the client. It would be rare for a counselor to be able to meet all the needs of a substance abusing client. Client strengths and weaknesses are many and varied, and therefore a counselor should feel continually challenged to think of the ways the client's varying needs can be met. It is not a sign of weakness to not be able to meet all of a client's needs, but rather it is wise to be able to recognize these needs and make an appropriate referral. As a supervisor myself, I worry about the entry-level counselor who does not ask questions related to referral. It is likely that one's "inner-voice" is speaking and saying something like "I'll look dumb if I ask that", or, "I should know that".

From the Client's Point of View

Clients will experience a variety of feelings when a referral is suggested by a counselor. Their feelings may range from anger to confusion to hope. Yet they will expect to be dealt with honestly and will likely respect their counselor if he or she admits to being limited in addressing particular problems. The more related the referral is to the specific reason for seeking treatment, the more understanding the client will be in accepting the referral.

From the Counselor's Point of View

Referral should be viewed as an important function for an alcohol and drug abuse counselor. No counselor can expect to do all things for all clients. A counselor must put one's training and experience in perspective and recognize his or her limits to perform within one's scope of practice. Failure to do so is not only unprofessional but also unethical and oftentimes illegal.

The first opportunity for making a referral with a client is during the screening function. A potential client makes contact with a counselor and during the screening the counselor determines whether the individual is eligible and appropriate for the counselor's program. If the client requires other services, it is appropriate to make a referral while explaining to the potential client the nature of the referral and answering why the referral will help the client.

Another opportunity for referral takes place during the intake function. If the potential client is not eligible or appropriate for the counselor's program, a referral should be made. A counselor may admit a client to the program and immediately see the need for referral for services from other professionals, for example, a client may need medical attention or assistance with housing or food.

Once the assessment is completed, most of the client's strengths, weaknesses, problems, and needs have likely been identified. The treatment plan developed by the counselor and the client may have identified a number of needs that the counselor or the program cannot meet. At this point a counselor will again need to be skillful in explaining to the client the nature and need for a referral in an understandable manner.

The need for referral, of course, may occur throughout the course of treatment. A need for referral may be recognized in counseling or during a crisis. If so, then an appropriate referral should be made.

Finally, a need for referral may be indicated as part of a discharge plan or aftercare plan. Again, the counselor explains the need for referral while having the client sign the appropriate authorizations for release of client identifying data.

Global Criteria

35. Identify need(s) and/or problem(s) that the agency and/or counselor cannot meet.

To be competent in this criterion, a counselor recognizes the client needs or problems that fall beyond the counselor's scope of practice as an alcohol and drug abuse counselor or the agency's program.

A counselor might relate referral to a specific client or to types of needs and problems, in general. For example, Victoria, a counselor at Pathways to Change Counseling Center, is neither a medical doctor nor does she have adequate training in psychopharmacology. Her client, Leslie, has a prescription for Valium, by her report, for "bad nerves." Since this falls outside Victoria's scope of training and experience, it is appropriate for Victoria to refer Leslie for further assessment of her "bad nerves."

36. Explain the rationale for the referral to the client.

To be competent in this criterion, a counselor understands the need to explain the nature of the referral, the rationale for the referral assesses whether the client understood the referral and responds to any questions or input.

Victoria might say to Leslie, "I'm not a medical doctor or psychiatrist. You tell me you take Valium for "bad nerves". I'd like you to see Dr. Jones, our consulting psychiatrist, who can best help you and determine what medication might be best for you".

37. Match client needs and/or problems to appropriate resources.

To be competent in this criterion, a counselor matches client needs or problems identified in Global Criterion 35 to appropriate services or resources, for example, an adult client might need a high school diploma. The appropriate match would be a referral to either vocational rehabilitation or to a community service that offered help for adults to obtain a GED.

38. Adhere to applicable laws, regulations, and agency policies governing procedures related to the protection of the client's confidentiality.

To be competent in this criterion, a counselor ensures that all aspects of the law regarding client confidentiality are adhered to and that the client signs a release of information form so that the referral can be completed. Agency policies are followed. It is important that the counselor not confuse referral with consultation when completing this criterion.

39. Assist the client in utilizing the support systems and community resources available.

To be competent in this criterion, a counselor facilitates the use of support systems and community resources with and for the client. For example, calling a community college together to ask for further information about obtaining a GED.

As I mentioned in Chapter 1, global criteria represent the skills considered important for a counselor to demonstrate competence in the 12 core functions. In the Certified Alcohol and Other Drug Abuse Counselor Job Task Analysis Report 2008 published by the IC&RC both knowledge AND skills were incorporated as tasks into 8 Performance Domains. It is important for the substance abuse counselor to be both knowledgeable AND skillful in his or her capacity as a substance abuse counselor. The core function of Referral is included in Domain 3, Referral and the following are the tasks in the Domain of Referral:

Domain 3: Referral

- Identify client needs which cannot be met in the current treatment setting.
- Match client needs with community resources considering client's abilities, gender, sexual orientation, developmental level, culture, ethnicity, age, and health status to remove barriers and facilitate positive client outcomes.
- Identify referral needs differentiating between client self-referral and direct counselor referral.
- Explain to the client the rationale for the referral to facilitate the client's participation with community resources.
- Continually evaluate referral sources to determine effectiveness and outcome of the referral.

Assignments

1. Identify the types of client needs and problems that fall beyond your current scope of training. What resources could you use for referral?

2. Develop your own script for explaining the need for a referral to a client in an understandable manner.

3. Develop a table or chart with two columns. On the left side make a listing of client needs and problems. On the right side list appropriate resources for referral.

4. Assume that you are an alcohol and drug abuse counselor in private practice and need to develop an information release form. Read the applicable laws regarding the release of client information and design your own information release form.

5. Write an agency policy regarding the release of information that could be included in a policy and procedures manual.

Notes

✳Chapter 12 - Reports and Record Keeping

IC&RC defines REPORTS and RECORD KEEPING as **charting the results of the assessment and treatment plan; writing reports, progress notes, discharge summaries, and other client-related data.**

TAP 21 includes the core function of REPORTS and RECORD KEEPING in Domain VII – DOCUMENTATION.

TAP 21 Definition of REPORTS and RECORD KEEPING: The recording of the screening and intake process, assessment, treatment plan, clinical reports, clinical progress notes, discharge summaries, and other client-related data.

Reports and record keeping are product-oriented administrative functions. Reports include such formal items as the written assessment, treatment plan and discharge report. Everything a counselor does for and with a client should be documented. The start of documentation is with the initial screening process. It continues with the administrative paperwork of intake and orientation. The assessment process requires a written report and the entire assessment should be documented with notes, tests and questionnaire results, plus counselor observations. The evaluations of other professionals on the treatment team also should be made part of the client record. The end result of the assessment is an assessment report. (This is further discussed in the core function of Assessment.)

The treatment plan (and its revisions) is a written formal document on which the treatment process is based. Each and every counseling session requires progress notes so that the client's progress in achieving treatment plan objectives is documented. Crisis intervention notes document the nature of the crisis and what the counselor did to alleviate the crisis. All referrals and consultations should be documented with signed forms, notes and recommendations. All required information releases should be a part of the client record along with referral letters and other correspondence on behalf of the client.

Preparing reports and record keeping is a frequent function of a substance abuse counselor. Although the majority of a counselor's time may be in the direct counseling function, all aspects of client treatment require some form of a report or record to be kept.

One common method of documentation is the Subjective, Objective, Assessment, and Plan (SOAP) case note format. In the "Subjective" section the counselor records what the client said during the counseling session and what points are made. Also, naming the specific objective that was a focus of the session is an appropriate comment to note in the "Subjective" section. The specific activities conducted during the session in support of the treatment plan should be included in this section. Do not interpret what the client said or evaluate the results of the activity in this section.

In the "Objective" section the counselor should record an objective impression of the client, for example, physical appearance, demeanor, and observed behavior displayed during the counseling session.

In the "Assessment" section the counselor should record in behavioral terms his or her clinical impressions of the client, for example, interpretation of the client's behavior, progress towards completion of objectives, and prognosis.

In the "Plan" section the counselor should record the plan for the next session or client need(s) that should be pursued through case management activities. This allows the counselor to be forward thinking in order to advance the client's progress. Also, it will help other members of the treatment team and future counselors to quickly see where a client is at a specific point in the treatment plan. This is especially important should the primary counselor be unavailable and another counselor needs to counsel the client.

It is generally accepted that reports and record keeping are a necessary function of being an alcohol and drug abuse counselor. Keeping records facilitates communication among the treatment team and is invaluable to other counselors who may see the client when the primary counselor is not available, or when the client is referred to another treatment service. Adequate reporting and record keeping also helps a counselor's supervisor provide skillful supervision of the counselor's work with the client. Without reports and records, an agency's license or funding would be in jeopardy.

Documents that reveal the identity, diagnosis, prognosis, or treatment of a client must be marked to indicate they are protected and unauthorized disclosure is prohibited. In the United States, the following statement may be used:

"Protected by 42 U.S.C. 290dd-3 and 290ee-3; unauthorized disclosure prohibited."

From the Client's Point of View

The client should see the process of client record keeping with each client-counselor interaction. Few clients question the need for a counselor to keep a record of what is happening in treatment and most expect that an evaluation will be done on them. Usually, a short comment during the initial assessment and again in the first counseling session about the counselor's need to make some notes in order to "keep things straight" is all that is needed to alleviate a client's concerns. If a client were concerned about the counselor keeping a record, this would both be diagnostic and perhaps an issue to pursue in treatment. If a client's concern about record keeping exceeds a passing comment, the counselor may want to consider a consultation for the possibility that the client has a dual diagnosis and may display the characteristics of paranoia.

From the Counselor's Point of View

If there is one function of an alcohol and drug abuse counselor's job that is spoken about with disdain, it's doing reports and keeping records – the paperwork. It is indeed a rare counselor that "likes" doing this function. Nevertheless, it is important for a counselor to demonstrate skill in this core function. I have known a number of good counselors who lost their positions because they minimized keeping adequate records.

Once a counselor understands the importance of reports and record keeping there is often acceptance of doing a good job of documentation. I have had the experience of doing a video deposition on my treatment of a client. With the camera rolling, I had only a distant memory of my counseling 18 months previous and, thank goodness, good SOAP notes of each session, plus letters to the client's family physician, as assistance in my testimony. Nearly each counseling session was questioned — not only what I did, but the client's response, and my ongoing evaluation.

Global Criteria

40. Prepare reports and relevant records integrating available information to facilitate the continuum of care.

To be competent in this criterion, a counselor knows the kinds of reports prepared during the various stages of treatment and know how the reports and other available information are integrated into the treatment plan in order to facilitate the client's care.

41. Chart pertinent ongoing information pertaining to the client.

To be competent in this criterion, a counselor knows how to chart ongoing information for a client and knows what information is important to document. It is the counselor's responsibility to personally understand not only how and what is necessary to chart, but also to have an understanding of why charting is important to the client and the treatment plan.

42. Utilize relevant information from written documents for client care.

To be competent in this criterion, a counselor understands how information from written documents are used to benefit the client. A counselor understands how a report from another professional is used to identify a client's problem or need. For example, a psychologist's evaluation might identify a number of client strengths and weaknesses that could then be incorporated into the treatment plan. A consultation with a psychiatrist or a nutritionist might be helpful in directly improving the client's mental or physical health. Or a probation officer's report or other legal document may be important when addressing aspects of the client's aftercare program.

As I mentioned in Chapter 1, global criteria represent the skills considered important for a counselor to demonstrate competence in the 12 core functions. In the Certified Alcohol and Other Drug Abuse Counselor Job Task Analysis Report 2008 published by the IC&RC both knowledge AND skills were incorporated as tasks into 8 Performance Domains. It is important for the substance abuse counselor to be both knowledgeable AND skillful in his or her capacity as a substance abuse counselor. The core function of Reports and Record Keeping is included in Domain 7, Documentation and the following are the tasks in the Domain of Documentation:

Domain 7: Documentation

- Protect client's rights to privacy and confidentiality according to best practices in preparation and handling of records, especially regarding the communication of client information with third parties.
- Obtain written consent to release information from the client and/or legal guardian, according to best practices and administrative rules, to exchange relevant client information with other service providers.
- Document treatment and continuing care plans that are consistent with best practices and applicable administrative rules.
- Document client's progress in relation to treatment goals and objectives.
- Prepare accurate and concise reports and records including recommendations, referrals, case consultations, legal reports, family sessions, and discharge summaries.
- Document all relevant aspects of case management activities to assure continuity of care.
- Document process, progress, and outcome measurements.

Assignments

1. Develop a lesson plan for you to use in teaching another counselor how to write SOAP notes on a client.

2. Defend the position that record keeping is an important function for the alcohol and drug abuse counselor.

3. You have just completed a crisis counseling session with a female client whose husband moved out of the house that morning and took their six-year-old son with him. Prepare a likely progress note of the crisis session.

4. Explain how information obtained from other professionals might assist you in counseling a client. Identify the professional and the type of information likely to be obtained, then relate it to your client.

Notes

Notes

Chapter 13 - Consultation

IC&RC defines CONSULTATION as **relating with counselors and other professionals in regard to client treatment (services) to assure comprehensive quality care for the client.**

TAP 21 includes the core function of CONSULTATION in Domain IV, Service Coordination and it incorporates three elements: Implementing the Treatment Plan; Consulting; and, Continuing Assessment and Treatment Planning

TAP 21 Definition of SERVICE COORDINATION: The administrative, clinical, and evaluative activities that bring the client, treatment services, community agencies, and other resources together to focus on issues and needs identified in the treatment plan. Service coordination, which includes case management and client advocacy, establishes a framework of action to enable the client to achieve specified goals. It involves collaboration with the client and significant others, coordination of treatment and referral services, liaison activities with community resources and managed care systems, client advocacy, and ongoing evaluation of treatment progress and client needs.

The most common type of consultation is a staff meeting where various aspects of a client's case are discussed by a counselor seeking additional input from other members of the treatment team or his or her clinical supervisor. Consultation may also involve other professionals outside of the counselor's agency or office. For example, a counselor may seek input from a psychologist, psychiatrist, dentist, probation officer, vocational rehabilitation counselor, or other professionals in the community in order to provide the best client care.

The client is seldom present when consultation takes place. Yet, important ideas are exchanged that can affect the client. Hence, it is important to document the consultation.

Program policy and licensing requirements usually require consultation documentation at some determined frequency, perhaps at least every 30, 60 or 90 days. Any revisions in the treatment plan that result from consulting with others, must of course, be recorded — along with any requests for the client to authorize the release of personally identifiable information.

Consultation within a counselor's agency does not require a specific release of information signed by the client. On the other hand, an authorization for the information release signed by the client is required if client information is to be released to individuals outside of the counselor's agency. No release is needed to consult with outside professionals when client-identifying data is not disclosed.

Recall the discussion in Chapter 11 on Referral. It is important not to confuse the consultation core function with those activities discussed in the referral core function.

From the Client's Point of View

Clients in residential treatment programs expect staff meetings and for their case to be discussed, while clients in out-patient programs or in treatment with sole practitioners may be unaware that consultation is likely to occur. Whatever the setting, when client identifying information is to be discussed with an outside source, the client needs to be informed and sign an information release form for that specific consultation. This includes situations where a counselor receives clinical supervision from another professional for licensing or insurance requirements.

If the counselor adequately explains the rationale for consultation, there should be little concern on the part of the client. Seeking consultation may actually increase the potency of the client-counselor relationship by helping the client know that the counselor is seeking information that is meant to help him or her. In light of the reason for consultation and the nature of the client's presenting problems and treatment plan, should there be any degree of concern, then the need for the consultation would need to be further explained by a counselor.

From the Counselor's Point of View

An important aspect of consultation is awareness by the counselor that he or she "doesn't know it all." It seems the more education a counselor has, the greater the recognition of the vast amount of knowledge yet to be learned — and what a counselor doesn't know can hurt a client. Any counseling performed beyond a counselor's scope of education and training is unethical and may even cause the counselor to be legally liable for damages and compensation. Unethical counselor actions also place the agency at legal risk.

Keep in mind that consultation is as much for client care as it is for professional growth. A mature and confident counselor will therefore consult with others and not be threatened by the realization that he or she is not knowledgeable or informed about everything. I am concerned about any counselor who does not ask for occasional consultation, especially when I am the supervisor. My thinking is that such a counselor either "knows it all" or is hesitant to possibly ask that proverbial "dumb" question with the irrational fear that I might judge them negatively.

Global Criteria

43. Recognize issues that are beyond the counselor's base of knowledge and/or skill.

To be competent in this criterion, a counselor understands the limitations of his or her own education, training, and experience. A counselor identifies those issues of a client that necessitate consulting with other professionals and then implement what was learned as a result of the consultation to assist the client. For example, a newly hired counselor may need to consult with other staff members and the clinical supervisor frequently in regard to agency and community resources available to clients; or, an experienced counselor might need to consult on issues of medical or psychiatric issues where the counselor is less knowledgeable. Another example would be in the area of sexual dysfunction that is very likely outside the counselor's area of expertise. When a client indicates any problem in this area, consultation and perhaps referral is required.

44. Explain the rationale for the consultation to the client, if appropriate.

To be competent in this criterion, a counselor understands when it is appropriate to provide a client with a rational or discussion regarding the counselor's need or desire to seek consultation. As previously stated, sharing can increase the potency attributed to the counselor by the client. It is just as important to know when not to provide a rationale to the client, for example, in cases of transference or counter-transference. It could do more harm to the client than be beneficial. One inappropriate comment to make to a client would be "You really remind me of my first wife....."

45. Consult with appropriate resources to ensure the provision of effective treatment services.

To be competent in this criterion, a counselor knows what specific resources are likely available to be used in consultation; why the consultation is needed to assist in client care; have an expectation for a positive outcome for the consultation; and adhere to applicable laws, regulations, and agency policies as appropriate for the consultation used. Resources available may be many and varied, for example, consultation may occur with other community agencies such as vocational rehabilitation, the probation office, or the agricultural extension service.

46. Adhere to applicable laws, regulations, and agency policies governing the disclosure of client-identifying data.

To be competent in this criterion, a counselor has an understanding of when the law, a regulation, or an agency policy calls for various types of consultation by a counselor. A critical element for obtaining authorization to release information on a client is whether or not identifying information on the client is going to be released. It is often possible to hold a consultation with outside resources and not reveal the client's name or other confidential information. For example, consultation with a physician regarding the impact of a particular medical condition or, the possible use of Antabuse when no information identifying the client is given, does not require client authorization for the consultation to occur. A counselor should have a clear understanding of when the release of information is needed. Confusing this issue would suggest that a counselor is less than competent in this global criterion.

As I mentioned in Chapter 1, global criteria represent the skills considered important for a counselor to demonstrate competence in the 12 core functions. In the Certified Alcohol and Other Drug Abuse Counselor Job Task Analysis Report 2008 published by the IC&RC both knowledge AND skills were incorporated as tasks into 8 Performance Domains. It is important for the substance abuse counselor to be both knowledgeable AND skillful in his or her capacity as a substance abuse counselor. The core function of

Consultation is included in Domain 4, Service Coordination and the following are the appropriate tasks in the Domain of Service Coordination:

Domain 4: Service Coordination

- Identify and maintain information about current community resources in order to meet identified client needs.
- Communicate with community resources concerning relevant client information to meet the identified needs of the client.
- Advocate for the client in areas of identified needs to facilitate continuity of care.
- Evaluate the effectiveness of case management activities through collaboration with the client, treatment team members, and community resources to ensure quality service coordination.
- Consult with the client, family, and concerned others to make appropriate changes to the treatment plan ensuring progress toward treatment goals.

Assignments

1.   Based upon your current level of education, training, and experience identify a number of issues that are beyond your base of knowledge or skill. Identify how you could address those issues.

2.   Identify resources both within and outside a typical treatment program and list how these resources might assist a client's treatment.

3.   Discuss when a release of information is required in order to consult with professionals outside the treatment agency.

4.   Discuss the ethical implications of providing services beyond your area of expertise and training.

5.   Develop your own script for explaining the rationale for consultation to a client in an understandable manner.

Notes

Notes

Notes

Notes

Notes